International Baccalaureate Standard Level Biolog

D1635146

Using this Revision Guide

Welcome to the International Baccalaureate Standard Level Biology Revision Guide, 2016 edition.

The format is clear, colourful and simple to follow. Key points, facts and principles are listed for easy learning, and diagrams are designed to make them easy to learn and reproduce in an exam. Remember that a clear diagram provides an instant essay plan therefore helping you to gain the extra mark for clarity and organisation.

Although the guide covers every aspect of the Standard Level course the layout does not follow the sequence of the syllabus. Instead it has been reorganised to follow a more developmental sequence as Chapters, starting with Mathematical Requirements, Molecular Biology, Cell Biology, Cell Metabolism, and Human Physiology. These are followed by Ecology, Genetics and finally Evolution and Biodiversity.

'*Pale blue boxes*' contain information that helps with understanding by providing additional information. However you do not need to learn this.

Other '*coloured boxes*', such as these green and yellow ones, contain information that you do need to know.

 This means you need to be able to '*draw*' the diagram or diagrams.

 This means you need to be able to '*identify*' the diagram when it is given in an exam question.

 '*Annotate*' means adding some further information to the labels.

This is **your** revision book, so every few pages are sets of '*Grey Box Questions*'. These contain simple questions and you should be able to complete these. The answers are at the end of the chapter.

> 24. What type of cell division do prokaryotic cells use?

In addition to these there are a few larger '*Revision*' boxes.

> Krebs Cycle

At the end of each chapter there are a number of Self-test Quizzes, containing '*multiple choice questions*'. A suggested way to approach revision would be to work your way through a chapter and test yourself with the Grey Box Questions. Then at a later date check how much you have really learnt by trying the Self-test Quizzes.

Remember that when you answer multiple choice questions NEVER choose the first one that sounds right. Examiners sometimes put in a trick answer as A or B. Always read ALL four answers and try to think of the reason why the other three are wrong. The answers are in **Appendix 1** on pages 210-12.

In Chapter 7, Genetics, there is a '*worked example*' for each section followed by a problem for you to practise. The answer is at the end of the chapter. Then at the end of the chapter there are a further 6 problems with the worked answers in **Appendix 2** on pages 213–15.

The '*External Exam Assessments*' are given in **Appendix 3** on page 216.

The extended response exam questions start with a '*Command Term*' and so it is essential that you understand what these mean as you will be expected to apply them in your answers. There are three levels of depth of treatment and are all given in **Appendix 4** on page 217.

Appendix 5 on pages 218–20 has model answers for '*Extended Response' answers* using some of these command terms.

Appendix 6 on page 221 gives you some advice on what you should, and what you should *not* take into your exams.

Interesting websites worth looking at are **http://www.sciencedaily.com** and also **http://www.sci-news.com/biology**.

I am grateful to Pam Watson, Senior Biology Technician, and Georgina Kemp, Assistant Biology Technician at Sevenoaks School, for their invaluable help with experiments and microscope slide photographs, and also to Tony Stuart for his idea for the diagram of the endosymbiotic theory. Thanks also to many people for generously allowing me to use their images.

I would greatly value any feedback on this Revision Guide so that later editions can continue to help students throughout the world. Please feel free to email me at Oxford Study Courses – osc@osc-ib.com.

Ashby Merson-Davies

Contents

Chapter One
Mathematical Requirements and Statistics

Many aspects of modern Biology require mathematical manipulation of data. This chapter looks at some basic maths along with graphs and statistics. Further information on this is available in the *Student Guide for Internal Assessment in Biology*.

Size units in Biology

Scientists now use the International System of units or SI units. Ones commonly used in Biology are:

Length
- **metre** or **m**
- **millimetre** or **mm** = 10^{-3} of a metre
- **micrometre** or **μm** = 10^{-6} of a metre or 10^{-3} of a millimetre
- **nanometre** or **nm** = 10^{-9} of a metre or 10^{-6} of a millimetre or 10^{-3} of a micrometre

Time
- **hour** or **h**
- **minute** or **min**
- **second** or **s**

Concentration
- **mol dm^{-3}**

Area
- **Square metre** or **m^2** etc

Volume
- **Cubic metre** or **m^3** etc

per
This is shown by a minus sign, e.g.
per second or s^{-1}
per square metre or m^{-2}
per cubic millimetre or mm^{-3}

Centimetre or **cm** (10^{-2} of a metre) is often used for convenience, especially when measuring volumes – cubic centimetre cm^3.

Relative sizes

Molecules	Membrane thickness	Viruses	Bacteria	Organelles	Cells
1nm	10nm	100nm	1μm	upto 10μm	upto 100μm

Scale bars

A scale bar is a short line usually drawn on an electron micrograph that will allow you to calculate the magnification of the photograph.

Using a scale bar to calculate magnification. (See photo on right.)
1. Measure the scale bar on the photograph in mm with your ruler.
   15mm
2. Convert these mm into the same units as the scale bar using the information above.
   15mm = 15000μm
3. Divide this number by the number on the scale bar.
   15000 ÷ 5 = 3000

Therefore magnification = 3000x.

1.1 Scale bar on an image

Calculating magnification

An alternative is that the image states the magnification. From this you can calculate the actual size.

Example:
The 'cell' on the right has been magnified 750x.
Calculate its actual length.

1. Measure the length of the cell.
   41mm
2. Divide this by the magnification.
   41 ÷ 750 = 0.055mm
3. Convert to a sensible unit.
   0.055mm × 1000 = 55μm

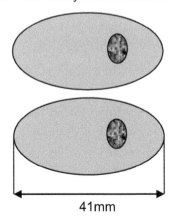

41mm

Averages

The term average is often used when talking about samples. There are three ways of measuring the average – **mean, median, and mode**. Which one is used depends on what you want to do with the data.

Calculating the mean

The mean is the sum of a set of values divided by the number of values. The mathematical symbols used have been standardised.
Each measurement or **value** from a sample is given the symbol x.
The sum of all measurements is written as Σx. (Σ is the Greek letter sigma).

The number of values in the sample is n.
The mean of the sample is x-bar, $\bar{x}$

The mean = $\dfrac{\text{sum of all samples}}{\text{sample size}}$ $\bar{x} = \dfrac{\Sigma x}{n}$

Most of the time you are calculating the **mean** and so use this word rather than average.

Calculating the median

This is the middle number for the results when arranged in rank order. (Remember median and middle).

Calculating the mode

This is the measurement that occurs the most number of times. (Remember mode and most).

Take the following set of results obtained from measuring the width of 10 beech leaves.

Raw data

Sample	Leaf width / cm ±0.5cm
1	1.6
2	1.4
3	1.7
4	1.4
5	1.4
6	2.0
7	1.2
8	1.6
9	1.8
10	1.5

The same data, but sorted into ascending rank order.

	Leaf width / cm ±0.5cm
	1.2
	1.4
	1.4
	1.4
	1.5
	1.6
	1.6
	1.7
	1.8
	2.0
mean	1.56
median	1.55
mode	1.4

Since there is an even number of samples the median is the mean between the fifth and sixth values when arranged in rank order.

Calculating a percentage

Suppose there are 15 students in your class and 11 of these are girls.
Calculate the percentage of girls in the class.

$\dfrac{\text{number of girls}}{\text{total number of students}} \times 100$ $\dfrac{11}{15} \times 100 = 73\%$

My calculator gives me the number 73.33333333. This should be rounded to a sensible number.

Calculating a percentage change

Suppose three more students joined your class after the start of term.
Calculate the percentage change in the number of students.

$$\frac{\text{change in number of students}}{\text{original number of students}} \times 100 \qquad \frac{3}{15} \times 100 = 20\% \text{ increase}$$

> The formula is always
> $\frac{\text{change}}{\text{original}} \times 100$
> Always state if the change is an increase or decrease.

However a little later 2 students left.
Calculate the percentage change in the number of students.

$$\frac{\text{change in number of students}}{\text{original number of students}} \times 100 \qquad \frac{2}{15} \times 100 = 13\% \text{ decrease}$$

Calculating a ratio

Key points
- Always bring one of the values to 1.
- This should be the first one stated in the ratio.

In a class of 28 students there are 11 girls and 17 boys.

What is the ratio of girls to boys?
$\frac{11 \text{ girls}}{11} = 1 \qquad \frac{17 \text{ boys}}{11} = 1.5$
The girl : boy ratio is 1 : 1.5

What is the ratio of boys to girls?
$\frac{17 \text{ boys}}{17} = 1 \qquad \frac{11 \text{ girls}}{17} = 0.6$
The boy : girl ratio is 1 : 0.6

Variables

There are four categories
- Independent – This is the one that is manipulated over a range of values.
- Dependent – This is the one that is measured.
- Controlled or Fixed – These are all the ones that are controlled at a fixed value.
- Uncontrolled – These are the ones that cannot be controlled.

Standard deviation

Key points
- Standard deviation is used to summarise the spread of values around the mean.
- A small value for standard deviation indicates that the data is close to the mean.
- A large value indicates that the data is spread out.
- If the standard deviation is greater than 33% of the mean then that is large.
- In a normal distribution:
  - 68% of the data falls within + or – one standard deviation of the mean,
  - 95% falls within + or – two standard deviations.
- Standard deviation has the same units as the values.

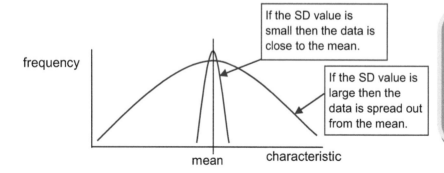

> If the SD value is small then the data is close to the mean.

> If the SD value is large then the data is spread out from the mean.

> **Example**
>
> Let us say the mean is 30 seconds and the standard deviation is 5 seconds.
>
> 68% of the values will fall within the times of 25 to 35 seconds, and 95% of the values will fall within the times of 20 to 40 seconds.

Calculating standard deviation

The symbol for standard deviation is **s** or sometimes σ.

❖ You should learn how to calculate standard deviation using your calculator.
❖ Remember that standard deviation has the same units as the data values.

When using your calculator to find standard deviation for a sample it may give you two possible standard deviations. Always choose the larger one as this uses n-1 rather than n. Likewise with other calculators if there is a key σ_{n-1} or s_{n-1} then use that in preference to σ_n or s_n.

> Take great care that any calculator you take into your IB exams is a permitted model – see Appendix 6 on page 221.

Graphs

Graphical representation of data allows for an easy interpretation of a set of data and also comparisons between sets of data. Bar charts, histograms and line graphs are the most common types but in Papers 2 and 3 expect to see some more unusual ones.

Bar charts

Key points
➢ Each set of data is represented by a bar which can go vertically or horizontally.
➢ There must be a space between each bar or groups of bars.

Example 1
A student set up clear glass dishes containing sugar water on different coloured backgrounds and counted the number of bees visiting each colour over a 2-hour period at midday.

Number of bees on each colour		
Red	Yellow	Blue
3	25	14

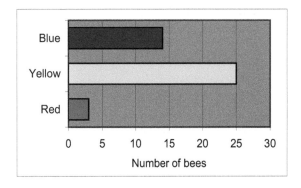

Example 2

A student noticed that several species of plant growing in a shaded woodland had leaves a different shade of green from members of the same species growing in a meadow. He made acetone extracts of the chloroplast pigments and measured the % light transmission using a colourimeter.

Plant species	% light transmission ±3%	
	Sun	**Shade**
A	45	61
B	36	40
C	22	59

Table 1. Colourimeter % transmission of acetone extracts from sun and shade leaves of three plant species.

Graph 1. Colourimeter % transmission of acetone extracts from sun and shade leaves of three plant species

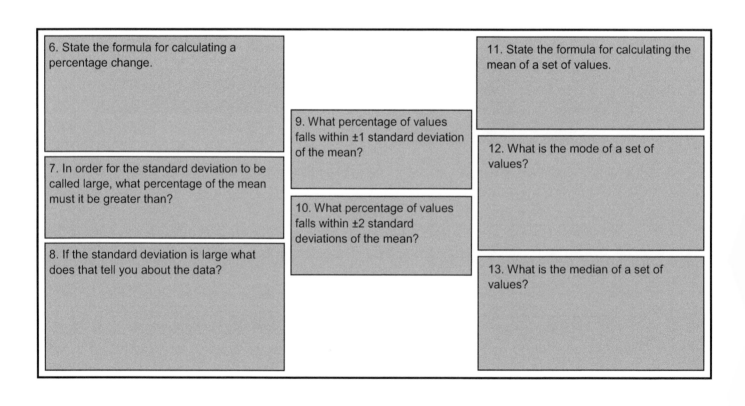

6. State the formula for calculating a percentage change.

7. In order for the standard deviation to be called large, what percentage of the mean must it be greater than?

8. If the standard deviation is large what does that tell you about the data?

9. What percentage of values falls within ±1 standard deviation of the mean?

10. What percentage of values falls within ±2 standard deviations of the mean?

11. State the formula for calculating the mean of a set of values.

12. What is the mode of a set of values?

13. What is the median of a set of values?

Histograms

Key points
➢ Also have a bar format.
➢ There is no space between each bar.
➢ The independent variable is continuous.

Example
A student collected the lengths of 24 leaves from each of two laurel bushes, one growing in a sunny environment and one in shade, and organised the data into groups as shown in the table below.

Leaf length / mm ±0.5mm	Number of leaves	
	sun	shade
90 – 94	2	1
95 – 99	3	1
100 – 104	3	2
105 – 109	5	4
110 – 114	4	7
115 – 119	3	7
120 – 124	3	5
125 – 129	1	3

Note that each set of values continues from the one before, i.e. 95 follows from 94 and 100 follows from 99, and each group is the same size.

Line graphs

Key points
➢ Plotting dependent variables against independent variables.
➢ Plotting one variable against another to show a correlation.
➢ The relationship can be linear or non-linear.

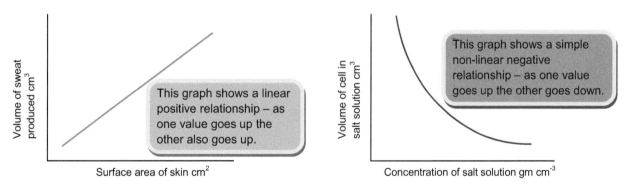

This graph shows a linear positive relationship – as one value goes up the other also goes up.

This graph shows a simple non-linear negative relationship – as one value goes up the other goes down.

Scattergraphs and correlation

Key points

➢ A scattergraph is a plot of two sets of variable data.

➢ The line may show a positive correlation, negative correlation or no correlation.

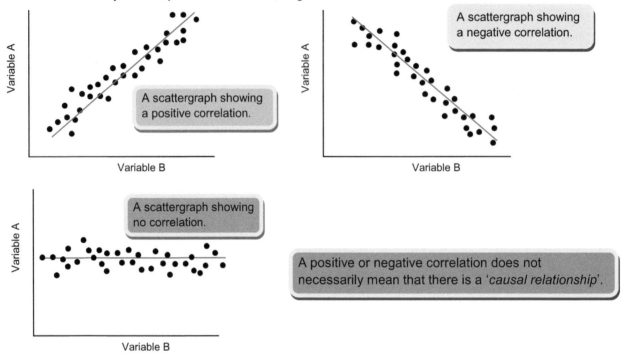

A scattergraph showing a positive correlation.

A scattergraph showing a negative correlation.

A scattergraph showing no correlation.

A positive or negative correlation does not necessarily mean that there is a 'causal relationship'.

- **Example 1**: In many countries obesity has increased and so has the incidence of type II diabetes, i.e. a positive correlation implying obesity causes diabetes. Experimental data would need to be collected to provide evidence that this is the case, and in fact this has proved to be correct.

- **Example 2**: Shale gas production in the USA has increased dramatically in the last few years and the population of honey bees has decreased dramatically – there is a negative correlation. However it would be unreasonable to state that the fall in honey bee populations has been caused by shale gas production.

Error bars

Key points

➢ Error bars show the variability or uncertainty in a set of data.

➢ This may take several forms such as simply the range of values, or standard deviation, or standard error of the mean.

Here is a basic table of some data.

	Data
	16
	18
	19
	15
	15
	17
	18
Mean	16.9
Standard deviation	1.6

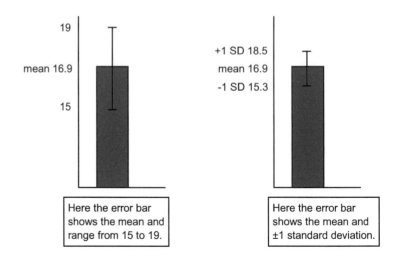

mean 16.9

Here the error bar shows the mean and range from 15 to 19.

+1 SD 18.5
mean 16.9
-1 SD 15.3

Here the error bar shows the mean and ±1 standard deviation.

IBSL Biology 2016 © Ashby Merson-Davies

> Error bars can be used when comparing sets of data.

For example data set A is without using a drug, the control. Data set B is using the drug.

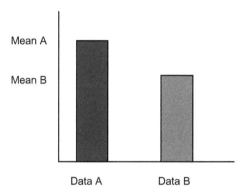

It appears that using the drug has an effect. However if we add error bars, say standard deviation, we can see that the upper values for data B overlap a lot with the lower values for data A. This indicates that the drug may not in fact be having an effect.

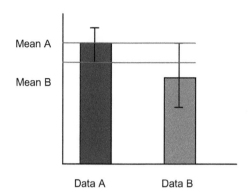

Hypotheses and significance testing

Hypotheses
A hypothesis is a prediction of the outcome of an investigation. There are two forms that the hypothesis can take and these are in opposition to each other. The statistical test you choose aims to prove one hypothesis right and the other one wrong.
The two forms of the hypothesis are the **null hypothesis**, H_0, and the **alternative hypothesis**, H_1.

The null hypothesis states that there is no link between the sets of data (observed and expected values), whereas the alternative hypothesis states that there is.

The null hypothesis is used if you are not able to predict a result.

Significance
> In biology 5% is taken as the boundary, meaning that the probability of the difference happening by chance is 5 times in 100.
> If the difference happens more than 5 times in 100, then it is due to chance.
> If the difference happens less than 5 times in 100, then it is probably due to a causal factor.
> Some statistics tests use tables of critical values and we compare the calculated result from a statistics test with the critical value.
> If the **calculated** value is **greater than** the **critical** value then the difference is **significant**, i.e. something has caused the difference.

Statistics – The chi-squared test

Key points
> This test compares the relationship between an observed set of data and an expected set of data.
> Each measurement must be independent from the others.
> The expected values must be greater than 5.

There are a great many statistical tests which can be used on collected data. One used in genetics and ecology is the chi-squared test.

Chi-squared in ecology
Key points
> In ecology it often is not possible to predict what the results should be as this would simply be guessing.
> Therefore we use the '**null hypothesis** and the statistics is used to prove or disprove it.
> The data is collected using quadrats positioned randomly in the sample area.
> In order to test for an association between two species, in each quadrat the number of both species is recorded.
> The data is recorded as a 2 × 2 contingency table.

The null hypothesis
This states that there is no difference between the observed and expected values.

Number of quadrats	Number of quadrats		Row totals
	Species A present	Species A absent	
Species B present	present / present	present / absent	
Species B absent	absent / present	absent / absent	
Column totals			**Grand total**

Adding the row totals **or** the column totals should give the same grand total.

A 2 × 2 contingency table   NB. The table must be set out in this way.

The formulae

To calculate the expected frequencies:

$$E = \frac{\text{row total} \times \text{column total}}{\text{grand total}}$$

To calculate degrees of freedom:

(number of rows − 1) × (number of columns − 1)

Again you need to know how to calculate degrees of freedom.

To calculate chi-squared:

$$\chi^2 = \sum \frac{(O - E)^2}{E}$$

Where
$\sum$ = sum of
O = the observed result
E = the expected result

Example

The diamond leaf willow (*Salix pulcha*) and the Arctic willow (*Salix arctica*) are both found on rocky outcrops in marshy ground in the Arctic tundra. A survey was carried out to see if there was an association between these two species.

Number of quadrats	Number of quadrats		Row totals
	S. pulcha present	*S. pulcha* absent	
S. arctica present	52	38	90
S. arctica absent	45	20	65
Column totals	97	58	**Grand total** 155

We now calculate the expected values, E.

Number of quadrats	Number of quadrats		Row totals
	S. pulcha present	*S. pulcha* absent	
S. arctica present	$\frac{90 \times 97}{155} = 56.3$	$\frac{90 \times 58}{155} = 33.7$	90
S. arctica absent	$\frac{65 \times 97}{155} = 40.7$	$\frac{65 \times 58}{155} = 24.3$	65
Column totals	97	58	**Grand total** 155

$$E = \frac{\text{row total} \times \text{column total}}{\text{grand total}}$$

Check that your expected row and column totals match the observed totals.

This data can now be entered into a standard chi-squared table

	O	E	O − E	$(O-E)^2$	$\frac{(O-E)^2}{E}$
Both present	52	56.3	-4.3	18.49	0.328
S. pulcha only	45	40.7	4.3	18.49	0.454
S. arctica only	38	33.7	4.3	18.49	0.549
Both absent	20	24.3	-4.3	18.49	0.761
Totals	155	155	0		$\sum$ = 2.09

    IBSL Biology 2016 © Ashby Merson-Davies

Degrees of freedom	Significance Level Probability				
	20% 0.2	10% 0.1	**5% 0.05**	2% 0.02	1% 0.01
1	1.64	2.71	**3.84**	5.41	6.64
2	3.22	4.61	**5.99**	7.82	9.21
3	4.64	6.25	**7.82**	9.84	11.34
4	5.99	7.78	**9.49**	11.67	13.28
5	7.29	9.24	**11.07**	13.39	15.09
	← decreasing		significance	increasing →	

Degrees of freedom = $(2 - 1) \times (2 - 1) = 1$

Table of chi-squared values

The null hypothesis, H_0, states that there is no association between the two *Salix* species.

The 5% critical value on the table for 1 degree of freedom is 3.84 Remembering that if the calculated value is **greater** than the critical value then the difference is significant. The calculated figure of 2.09 is smaller than this so the observed difference is not significant. We would accept the null hypothesis – there is no association between the two species of *Salix*.

You can check your calculations very quickly by going to:

http://www.physics.csbsju.edu/stats/contingency_NROW_NCOLUMN_form.html

Enter 2 and 2 for the rows and columns, click submit, enter your 4 observed values and click calculate now. Make sure you match the number to the box as putting the values in different positions may give the wrong calculation. This gives you the expected numbers, the chi-squared value and the probability.

Nomograms

Key points

➢ A nomogram is a group of three or more scales.
➢ Each scale shows a different set of values.
➢ Data is collected for two of the values and these are used to read off a value on the third scale.
➢ The scales can be positioned vertically or horizontally

Example

Scale 1   Scale 2   Scale 3

Given value for scale 1 = 6.0 units,
Given value for scale 3 = 20.0 units,
Draw a straight line between these two values,
Read off scale 2 value = 13.1 units.

Glossary

CAUSAL RELATIONSHIP	A relationship between one event, X, and another, Y, in which X precedes and causes Y.
CORRELATION	A relationship between two variables where a change in one causes a corresponding or proportional change in the other values.
ERROR BAR	Used on a graph to show some measure of upper and lower values about the mean. Commonly this is standard deviation.
HYPOTHESIS	A testable explanation of an observed event.
QUADRAT	A measured square area which encloses a sampling area.
NORMAL DISTRIBUTION	A bell shaped curve on a graph which is symmetrical each side of the mean.
NULL HYPOTHESIS	Used in statistics, this states that there is no difference between the observed and predicted values.
SIGNIFICANCE	In a statistics test the significance is whether one variable has an effect on another variable or if the result is simply due to chance, In Biology the most common level of significance is 5%, i.e. if the investigation was carried out 100 times then it is acceptable to have 5 of them where the effect was due to chance.
STANDARD DEVIATION	A statistical measure of the spread of data about the mean of a set of values with a normal distribution. 68% of the values fall within ±1 standard deviation of the mean, 95% of the values fall within ±2 standard deviations of the mean.

Answers to Grey Box Questions

1. $22000\mu m$
2. 10^6
3. 10^3
4. a. Measure the scale bar on the photograph in mm.
   b. Convert these mm into the same units as the scale bar.
   c. Divide this number by the number on the scale bar.
5. $mm^3\ min^{-1}$
6. $\dfrac{\text{difference in values}}{\text{original value}} \times 100$
7. 33%
8. It is spread out on either side of the mean.
9. 68%
10. 95%
11. total of all the values ÷ number of values
12. the most frequent value
13. the middle value

Self-test Quiz

1. Which line in the table is correct?

	Molecules	Membrane thickness	Viruses	Bacteria	Organelles	Cells
a.	1μm	10nm	1μm	Upto 10μm	10nm	Upto 100μm
b.	10nm	1μm	100nm	100nm	Upto 10μm	Upto 100μm
c.	1nm	10nm	Upto 10μm	1μm	Upto 100μm	100nm
d.	1nm	10nm	100nm	1μm	Upto 10μm	Upto 100μm

2. Determine the magnification of these scale bars.

Determine the magnification of these scale bars. The answers are at the bottom of the page.

a. 2μm   b. 3μm   c. 1μm

3. Calculate the actual size of these drawings.

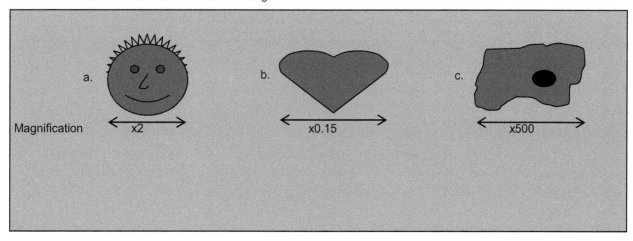

a.   b.   c.

Magnification   x2   x0.15   x500

4. Use the data in the table to calculate the mean, median and mode.

	height of student / m
	1.5
	1.6
	1.6
	1.7
	1.9
	2.0
mean	
median	
mode	

5. The number of bacterial colonies on a petri dish on day 1 was 12 and on day 2 was 35. Determine the percentage change in the number of colonies.

6. In a new forest plantation there are 376 planted forest trees and 85 self-seeded trees. Determine the ratio of self-seeded to forest trees.

7. Use your calculator to calculate the mean and standard deviation of the following data.

Set 1 mm	Set 2 mm	Set 3 mm	Set 4 mm	Set 5 mm	Mean	Standard deviation
13	12	15	14	11		

8. Which type of correlation does the graph below show?

Variable B

9. A student calculated the mean and standard deviation for a set of measurements of light transmission through an extract of anthocyanin, a red plant pigment. She found the mean value was 47% with a standard deviation of 13%. Was she right in stating that the standard deviation was very small?

10. Standard deviation can be applied to a population with a normal distribution. In this case:
    a. 68% of the population falls within ± 1 standard deviation of the mean,
    b. 95% of the population falls within ± 1 standard deviation of the mean,
    c. 68% of the population fits under the curve,
    d. 68% of the population falls within ± 2 standard deviation of the mean.

11. Population A has a standard deviation of 2.7 units and population B has a standard deviation of 3.2 units. It can be deduced that:
    a. Population A is smaller than population B.
    b. The mean value of population B is greater than the mean value of population A.
    c. Population B shows greater variation than population A.
    d. The sampling procedure used for population A was different from that used for population B.

12. To measure growth rate an apple grower collected 1000 apples from trees in one of his fields. Assuming the sample had a normal distribution how many apples would be within two standard deviations of the mean?
    a. 680,
    b. 950,
    c. 500,
    d. 475.

13. The apple grower also wanted to compare the productivity of the same apple variety growing in two different fields. The table shows the data he collected.

	Mean number of apples per tree	Number of trees sampled	Standard deviation
Field A	350	1000	7.1
Field B	300	800	2.5

Which of the following statements is correct?
    a. The results from field A are more accurate because a larger number of trees was sampled.
    b. The results from field A are more reliable because the standard deviation is higher.
    c. Only the results from field B have a normal distribution.
    d. The trees in field B each have a number of apples closer to the mean than the trees in field A.

IBSL Biology 2016 © Ashby Merson-Davies

14a. On the island of Madeira water channels called levadas have been cut into the rock to provide water for irrigation. Over time the cut rock surfaces have become covered by a growth of mosses and liverworts. A student wanted to find out if there was an association between the mosses and liverworts and so she collected the following data:

- Rock surfaces with both moss and liverwort – 120
- Rock surfaces with only moss – 46
- Rock surfaces with only liverwort – 29
- Rock surfaces with neither moss nor liverwort – 5

Draw a contingency table for this data.

14b. Calculate the expected values based on the null hypothesis.

14c. Calculate the number of degrees of freedom.

14d. Calculate the chi-squared value and state whether the null hypothesis has been rejected or accepted.

	Observed O	Expected E	O – E	$(O-E)^2$	$\dfrac{(O-E)^2}{E}$
Both moss and liverwort	120				
Moss only	46				
Liverwort only	29				
Neither	5				
Totals	*200*	*200*	*0*		

	Significance Level Probability				
Degrees of freedom	20% 0.2	10% 0.1	5% 0.05	2% 0.02	1% 0.01
1	1.64	2.71	3.84	5.41	6.64
2	3.22	4.61	5.99	7.82	9.21
3	4.64	6.25	7.82	9.84	11.34
4	5.99	7.78	9.49	11.67	13.28
5	7.29	9.24	11.07	13.39	15.09

Table of chi-squared values

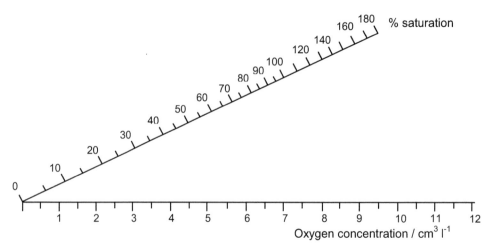

Use the nomogram above to answer the following.

15a. If the temperature of the water is 15°C what is the % saturation when the oxygen concentration is 4cm³ l⁻¹?

15b. Determine the temperature change that causes a change in % saturation from 25 to 35 while the oxygen concentration remains at 2cm³ l⁻¹.

16. The number of peas in a sample of 10 pods was counted and the data shown in the table.

1	2	3	4	5	6	7	8	9	10	Mean
5	6	6	7	7	7	7	8	8	9	7

What is the best estimate of the standard deviation?
 a. 5
 b. 9
 c. 7
 d. 1

17. The Carrot Root fly lays its eggs in the soil around the carrot plant. Soil samples were collected from 10 plants and the number of eggs counted. The data is shown in the table:

1	2	3	4	5	6	7	8	9	10	Mean	Standard deviation
44	52	71	45	69	72	83	68	75	81	66	14.1

What statistical percentage of the soil samples has between 52 and 80 eggs?
 a. 14.1%
 b. 33%
 c. 68%
 d. 95%

18. What do error bars on graphs indicate?
 a. The variability of the data.
 b. The method used to collect the data.
 c. The statistical analysis used on the data.
 d. The result which is closest to the mean value.

Chapter Two
Molecular Biology Part 1
Carbon, water, carbohydrates, lipids

Molecular Biology looks at four major groups
of biological molecules – carbohydrates, lipids,
proteins and nucleic acids.
All organic molecules are based on the carbon atom.

Molecules

Key points
- Living organisms are made up from only a small proportion of all the elements.
- The four most common elements are carbon, hydrogen, oxygen and nitrogen.
- Other important elements include calcium, sodium, potassium, phosphorus, sulphur, and iron.
- Elements are bonded together to form compounds.
- Organic compounds are those that contain carbon, but excluding carbonates, hydrogen carbonates and oxides of carbon, e.g. carbon dioxide.
- All other compounds are inorganic, e.g. water.
- Living organisms are made up of both inorganic and organic compounds.
- The four major groups of organic carbon compounds are:
  - carbohydrates,
  - lipids,
  - proteins,
  - nucleic acids.
- Living processes are the result of chemical interactions.
- Molecular biology can explain these interactions.
- Urea   - is an organic compound that is produced by living organisms,
               - can by synthesised artificially.

Hydrophilic and hydrophobic
Chemical substances can be hydrophilic or hydrophobic.
- A hydrophilic substance has an affinity for and interacts with water through hydrogen bonding.
- A hydrophobic substance will not interact with water.

> Examples of hydrophilic substances:
> - sugars,
> - salts,
> - vitamin C.

> Examples of hydrophobic substances:
> - Fats,
> - vitamins A, D and E.

Amphipathic
An amphipathic molecule has part of it hydrophilic and part hydrophobic.

> Example of an amphipathic substance:
> - phospholipid.

> Hydro = water
> philic = like
> phobic = hate

Carbon

Key points

- The dark grey ball is the carbon atom.
- The pale grey balls are other atoms that can be bonded on.
- Carbon atoms can form four covalent bonds shown in black.
- These bonds may be single as in methane CH_4, or double as in carbon dioxide CO_2, or even a mixture as in fatty acids – see page 22.
- This allows carbon to form a large diversity of stable compounds.

Water

Key facts
- Water is a dipolar molecule – it has negative and positive ends (poles).
- The oxygen atom has a slight negative charge.
- The hydrogen atoms each have a slight positive charge.
- The positive and negative charges on different molecules attract each other.
- This attraction forms hydrogen bonds ┄┄┄┄
- This is called **cohesion**.
- The polarity of water allows it to dissolve other polar molecules such as sugars and amino acids with polar side groups.
- Other substances form ions in water and dissolve, e.g. sodium chloride (salt) forms sodium ions Na^+ and chloride ions Cl^-.
- Water is also attracted to other molecules.
- This is called **adhesion**.
- Water has a high specific heat, i.e. it can store a large amount of heat.
- Water has a high latent heat of vaporisation, i.e. it takes a lot of energy to turn liquid water to water vapour.
- Water has a high density.

Comparing the thermal properties of water and methane

	Water	Methane
Chemical formula	H_2O	CH_4
Hydrogen bonding	Yes	No
Latent heat of vaporisation	$2,257J\ g^{-1}$	$760J\ g^{-1}$
Boiling point	100^0C	-161^0C

When a liquid boils the molecules evaporate. The difference in boiling point and latent heat of vaporisation clearly shows the significance of the hydrogen bonding.
A much greater input of energy is required before the water molecules evaporate compared to methane which, because it is non-polar, does not have hydrogen bonding.

Water as a heat transporter
Significant property
- ❖ High specific heat.
  - ➢ Plasma forms 55% of the blood.
  - ➢ Plasma is 92% water.
  - ➢ Heat can be transported from a hotter part of the body to a cooler part.

Example:
A lizard sunbathing in the morning can transport heat absorbed through the skin to its internal organs.

Water as a habitat
Significant property
- ❖ High specific heat.
  - ➢ A large amount of heat energy is required to warm water.
  - ➢ It loses this heat energy slowly.
  - ➢ This makes water a very stable habitat.

Water as a coolant
Significant properties
- ❖ High specific heat.
- ❖ High latent heat of vaporisation.
  - ➢ When water is in a liquid form the molecules are held together by hydrogen bonding.
  - ➢ When water evaporates these hydrogen bonds are broken.
  - ➢ Breaking the bonds requires energy.
  - ➢ Heat energy is transported to the skin surface in the blood.
  - ➢ This heat energy is used to break the hydrogen bonds in the sweat on the skin surface and this cools the blood.

2.1 Beads of sweat show on this woman's back

Water as a transporter in blood
Significant property
- ❖ Polar solvent.
  - ➢ Polar substances such as sugars and amino acids readily dissolve.
  - ➢ Non-polar molecules such as fats and cholesterol (mostly non-polar) are transported as lipoproteins – see page 23.

Water as a transporter in plants
Significant properties
- ❖ Polar solvent:
  - ➢ Polar substances such as sucrose, amino acids and mineral salts readily dissolve in the water of the phloem sap and the water in the xylem vessels.
- ❖ Adhesion:
  - ➢ Water molecules are attracted to the surface of the xylem vessel wall.
  - ➢ Water molecules move from the xylem vessels to the mesophyll cell surface through cell walls.
  - ➢ Cellulose cell walls have molecule sized channels.
  - ➢ This small channel size creates very high adhesive forces.
- ❖ Cohesion:
  - ➢ As water molecules evaporate from the surface of a leaf cell further water molecules are pulled from behind creating the transpiration stream in the xylem.

water vapour in air space in leaf

wall of leaf mesophyll cell

cytoplasm

xylem vessel transporting water from the roots

↑ cohesive forces

↑ adhesive forces

channel in cellulose

Simple diagram of leaf to show the role of cohesive and adhesive forces in transporting water

Carbohydrates

These include:

- sugars – monosaccharides and disaccharides,
- starch,
- glycogen, ⎤
- cellulose. ⎦ polysaccharides

D-ribose

alpha-D-glucose

beta-D-glucose

The difference between alpha and beta glucose
Imagine the ring as lying horizontally.
Note the position of the hydroxyl group –OH on carbon 1.
In alpha glucose it is below the ring and in beta glucose it is above the ring.
In alpha glucose the hydroxyl groups are down, down, up, down – DDUD.
In beta glucose the hydroxyl groups are up, down, up, down – UDUD.

Monosaccharides and disaccharides

Key points

➤ Monosaccharides have a single ring of carbon atoms.
➤ Glucose and ribose are monosaccharides.
➤ Ribose is a pentose because it has 5 carbon atoms.
➤ Glucose is a hexose because it has 6 carbon atoms.
➤ Two monosaccharide monomers (hexoses) are joined by condensation to form a disaccharide – see page 25.

Two monosaccharides form a disaccharide

Monosaccharides
Glucose
Galactose
Fructose

Disaccharides
Maltose = glucose + glucose
Lactose = glucose + galactose
Sucrose = glucose + fructose

Polysaccharides

Definition

➤ More than two monosaccharides joined to form a chain.

Polysaccharides
Starch
Cellulose ⎤= poly-glucose
Glycogen ⎦

1-4 and 1-6 linkage mean that carbon 1 of one monosaccharide is linked to either carbon 4 or carbon 6 of the other monosaccharide.

	Structure	Function
Cellulose	Made of polyglucose residues – see page 25, Uses beta-D-glucose, Joined by a 1-4 linkage, Unbranched, Straight chains, Chains cross-linked by hydrogen bonding, Very strong.	Cell wall of plant cells, Supports plant, Porous and allows water to flow through it.
Starch	Polyglucose residues, Uses alpha-D-glucose, Joined by a 1-4 linkage, Two forms – amylose and amylopectin, Amylose is unbranched, Amylopectin is slightly branched using 1-6 linkages, Both forms are coiled, Insoluble.	Energy storage molecule in plants, Both forms found together in starch grains.
Glycogen	Made of polyglucose residues, Uses alpha-D-glucose, Joined by a 1-4 linkage, Profusely branched using 1-6 linkages, Insoluble.	Energy storage molecule in animals, Stored in liver and skeletal muscle cells, Forms tiny granules in cytoplasm.

Cellulose

Cellulose is very strong due to the large numbers of hydrogen bond crosslinks between the strands.

These are possible due to the beta-D-glucose molecules which have to alternate position in order to form the 1 – 4 linkages.

Starch

Starch obtained from potatoes is used as an adhesive;
The presence of amylose reduces the adhesive property;
Potatoes have been genetically modified to reduce the amylose content.

Amylose is unbranched;
Amylopectin is slightly branched using 1-6 linkages.

Branching occurs using a 1 – 6 condensation linkage.

Lipids

These include:

- triglycerides,
- phospholipids,
- steroids.

Triglycerides

Key points

Composed of:

- glycerol,
- three fatty acids,
- the fatty acids may be saturated, monounsaturated or polyunsaturated,
- triglycerides are formed by condensation – see page 25.

Glycerol residue | Fatty acid residues

A triglyceride

Fatty acid structure

Key facts

$CH_3 \!-\! (CH_2)_n \!-\! COOH$ $HOOC \!-\! (CH_2)_n \!-\! CH_3$

Three different ways of writing the structure of a fatty acid.

n is a variable number, around 14-24 in biological molecules.

- ➤ Saturated fatty acids have no double bonds between the carbon atoms of the $-CH_2$ region.
- ➤ Unsaturated fatty acids have one or more double bonds between the carbon atoms.
- ➤ Mono-unsaturated fatty acids have only one double bond.
- ➤ Polyunsaturated fatty acids have two or more double bonds.

Draw

Identify

A saturated C7 fatty acid

- ➤ **Cis** means the hydrogen atoms are on the same side on each side of a double bond.

Cis

- ➤ **Trans** means the hydrogen atoms are on opposite sides on each side of a double bond.

Trans

A polyunsaturated C9 cis fatty acid

Hint – to transverse means to go **across**.

Phospholipids
Key point

- ➢ This is a modified triglyceride.
- ➢ The third fatty acid has been replaced by a phosphate group.
- ➢ Phospholipids are a major component of membranes – see page 66.

This region is hydrophobic

This region is hydrophilic

A phospholipid

Steroids

Identify

F

The simplest steroid

> The characteristic structure of steroids is three six sided rings and one five sided ring.
> There can be a functional group F attached to the five sided ring to form the different types of steroid. (This is like the R group of amino acids).

Carbohydrates and lipids as energy stores

Carbohydrates
⇒ 17kJ of energy released per gram;
⇒ Easily built up for storage;
⇒ Easily broken down to release energy quickly;
⇒ Glycogen in animals: starch in plants;
⇒ Both of these converted to glucose when energy required.

Lipids
⇒ 38kJ of energy released per gram – over twice as much,
⇒ hence more efficient as energy store,
⇒ storage efficiency increased because lipids are hydrophobic and less mass is taken up storing water;
⇒ Metabolic pathways to build up and break down more complex and therefore slower,
⇒ Converted to fatty acids and glycerol when energy required.

Scientific evidence for health risks of trans fats and saturated fatty acids
Key facts

- ➢ High levels of LDL (see blue box) in the blood stream increase the risk of coronary heart disease due to atherosclerosis – see page 117.
- ➢ Some studies have shown that trans fats and saturated fats in the diet increase the levels of LDL and lower the levels of HDL.
- ➢ In November 2014 research published by Ohio State University showed that a diet high in saturated fat but low in carbohydrate did not raise LDL as the fats were used for energy production. On the other hand a high carbohydrate / low saturated fat diet increased levels of LDL.

> **LDL and HDL**
> Fats are insoluble and cholesterol is only very slightly soluble. They are carried in the blood as tiny lipoprotein particles. There are two main types of lipoprotein – HDL (high density lipoprotein) and LDL (low density lipoprotein). Fats are less dense than water so LDL particles contain a high proportion of fat and cholesterol.
> LDLs are referred to as 'bad' cholesterol and HDLs as 'good' cholesterol.

Evaluation of evidence for health claims about lipids
For

- ➢ Several studies have shown that rTFAs (see second blue box) could be beneficial by lowering LDL.
- ➢ Studies in rodents showed that CLA was highly effective in reducing the development of arterial plaques.
- ➢ Two Kenyan tribes have a diet rich in saturated fatty acids yet coronary heart disease is very rare.

> **Trans fatty acids**
> Trans fatty acids, TFAs, are uncommon in nature but two particular types, VA and CLA, are found in beef and dairy products. These are rTFAs (r for ruminant).
> Most TFAs are manufactured from liquid cis fats such as vegetable oils to make them solid for food production. These are iTFAs (i for industrial).

Against

> All studies have shown that iTFAs increase plasma LDL increasing the risk of coronary heart disease.

> A study by the US Department of Agriculture showed that VA raised LDL but also raised HDL.

Conclusions

> Although there is a positive correlation between coronary heart disease and certain dietary fatty acids there is insufficient evidence for a causal link.

> The presence or absence of other dietary components such as fibre could modify the effect.

> In view of the variability of evidence and lack of agreement amongst researchers, along with lack of sufficiently controlled studies on humans it is recommended that trans fats are excluded from the diet.

Methods used to obtain evidence

Research using humans
- The sample needs to be very large to allow for genetic variability.
- The sample should be selected for similarities in age, gender, state of health and life style.
- Allowance must be made for peoples' honesty and accuracy in reporting their dietary intake.
- Does the statistical analysis show a wide variation making it less reliable?
- Are any statistical differences significant?

Research using animals
- Animals can be selected to be genetically uniform.
- Diets, environment, exercise can be carefully controlled.
- Trials using animals should only be done if no other methods are available.
- The importance of the results must be significant enough to justify animal experimentation.
- Any procedures used must avoid causing suffering.
- Anaesthetics should be used to prevent suffering.
- Animals should not be collected from the wild.

Condensation and hydrolysis

Key points

> Many macromolecules or polymers can be built up from monomer building blocks and similarly broken back down into the constituent monomers.

> Building up is by **condensation** – water is released.

> Breaking down is by **hydrolysis**.

> In some cases an 'O' and an 'OH' are used to make the water; in other cases two 'OH' groups are used. In the latter case the extra oxygen joins the two monomer residues.

Basic principles

Monomers and residues

A monomer is the individual building unit, e.g. a glucose or an amino acid.

Residue is a term used when part of a monomer has been lost during formation by condensation of a dimer/polymer. For example when two glucose monomers form a maltose dimer one glucose loses an H becoming $C_6H_{11}O_6$, and the other an OH becoming $C_6H_{11}O_5$.

Condensation and hydrolysis in carbohydrates

Two monosaccharides

Hydrolysis

Condensation

Disaccharide

Repeated condensation reactions build up a polysaccharide.

Condensation and hydrolysis in lipids

Glycerol + fatty acid

Hydrolysis

Condensation

Monoglyceride

Diglyceride

Triglyceride

Condensation and hydrolysis in amino acids

Two amino acids

Hydrolysis

Condensation

Dipeptide

Repeated condensation reactions build up a polypeptide. This is translation and occurs on the ribosomes – see page 44–5.

Body mass index (BMI)

Equation

$$BMI = \frac{mass\ in\ kg}{(height\ in\ m)^2}\ kg\ m^{-2}$$

BMI kg m^{-2}	Status
Below 18.5	Underweight
18.5 – 24.9	Normal
25.0 – 29.9	Overweight
Over 30.0	Severely overweight / obese

You are expected to know the equation and how to use a nomogram – revise page 12.

When a person has been diagnosed as obese by a doctor they are called **clinically obese**.

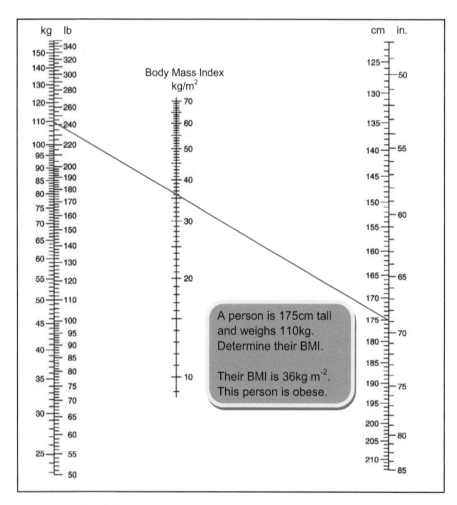

A person is 175cm tall and weighs 110kg. Determine their BMI.

Their BMI is 36kg m^{-2}. This person is obese.

2.2 These two photographs illustrate the increasing problem of obesity.

Are you the right weight?

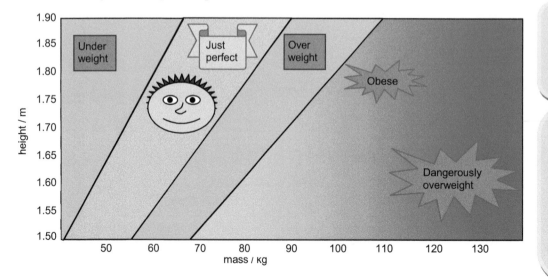

There is increasing evidence that epigenetic modification during fetal growth can result in the development of childhood obesity.

A report in *The Lancet Diabetes and Endocrinology* in December 2014 found a positive correlation between age, obesity and reduced life expectancy. Being obese at an age of 20-39 could reduce life expectancy by up to 9 years in men and 7.5 years in women.

IBSL Biology 2016 © Ashby Merson-Davies

Molecular visualisation software

Molecular visualisation software is used to produces models of molecules that can be manipulated in various ways, including rotating them to show their 3D structure.

This is a model of a triglyceride taken from http://biomodel.uah.es/en/model3/tag.htm
(You do not need to know any names or details from this example).

palmitic acid – saturated

oleic acid – mono-unsaturated

stearic acid – saturated

glycerol   double bond

The double bond causes the oleic acid to bend as shown below by rotating the model.

The chain is bent if it is a cis fatty acid, i.e. the hydrogens are on the same side of the carbon chain. This can clearly be seen in the red oval.

This bent fatty acid means the chains cannot pack so tightly in the phospholipid bilayer which makes the membrane more fluid which is especially important for on the rER and Golgi apparatus, and for endocytosis and exocytosis – see page 71.

1. What does hydrophobic mean?

2. What does amphipathic mean?

3. State an example of an amphipathic molecule.

6. Is hydrogen carbonate an organic or inorganic molecule?

9. How many covalent bonds can carbon form?

4. List the four most common elements used by organisms.

7. List the four major groups of organic compounds.

10. What property of water makes it good at transferring heat?

5. Which one is branched – amylose or amylopectin?

8. Distinguish between adhesion and cohesion.

11. What property of water makes it good as a coolant?

13. Identify this molecule.

14. Draw lines to link the sugar to its pattern of hydroxyl groups.
alpha-D-glucose   up down up down

beta-D-glucose   down down up down

12. What property do sugars have which allow them to dissolve in water?

15. State the missing sugar.
Maltose = glucose +

Lactose = glucose +

Sucrose = glucose +

16. Which molecule, alpha-D-glucose or beta-D-glucose is used to make cellulose?

17. Which molecule, alpha-D-glucose or beta-D-glucose is used to make starch?

18. List the components of a triglyceride.

19. Name the type of reaction used to build a triglyceride.

20. Name the type of reaction used to join monosaccharides together.

21. Which sugar, amylose or amylopectin, reduces the adhesive property of a starch paste?

22. What feature of cellulose makes it such a strong structure?

23. Draw the trans form of a fatty acid chain.

24. Draw a saturated fatty acid containing 4 carbon atoms.

25. State an example of a carbohydrate monomer.

27. What is the characteristic feature of an unsaturated fatty acid chain?

28. Draw a beta-D-glucose molecule.

26. List the components of a phospholipid.

Glossary

Adhesion	Attraction between water molecules and different molecules.
Cohesion	Hydrogen bonding between water molecules.
Compound	A substance made from two or more elements chemically combined.
Covalent bond	A strong chemical bond between molecules, eg between the sugar and phosphate and the sugar and base in a nucleotide.
Element	A substance which cannot be broken down into a simpler substance, eg. phosphorus P, calcium, Ca.
Hydrogen bond	A weak chemical bond between the weak positive charge on a hydrogen atom and the weak negative charge on either an oxygen or a nitrogen atom.
Hydrophilic	Having an affinity for water.
Hydrophobic	A reluctance to mix with water.
Ion	A charged particle, e.g. sodium ion Na^+, chloride ion Cl^-, phosphate ion PO_4^{3-}.
Latent heat of vaporisation	The amount of heat energy required to convert a liquid into a vapour.
Lysis	Splitting.
Phloem	A system of modified cells in plants that form tubes which transport dissolved organic materials up and down the plant.
Polar molecule	A molecule in which the electric charge is not distributed evenly in the covalent bonds.
Polar solvent	A substance that will dissolve polar molecules.
Specific heat	The amount of heat that must be absorbed by 1g of a substance to raise its temperature by 1^0C.
Xylem	A system of modified cells in plants that form tubes which transport water and dissolved minerals from the soil up into the plant.

Answers to Grey Box Questions

1. Water hating.
2. Having both hydrophilic and hydrophobic regions.
3. Phospholipid.
4. Carbon, hydrogen, oxygen, nitrogen.
5. Amylopectin.
6. Inorganic.
7. Carbohydrates, lipids, proteins, nucleic acids.
8. Adhesion – an attraction between different types of molecule; cohesion – an attraction between the same type of molecule.
9. 4.
10. High specific heat.
11. Cohesion.
12. They are polar.
13. Ribose.
14.

15. Maltose – glucose.
    Lactose – galactose.
    Sucrose – fructose.
16. Beta-D-glucose.
17. Alpha-D-glucose.
18. Glycerol + **three** fatty acids.
19. Condensation.
20. Condensation.
21. Amylose.
22. Numerous hydrogen bond cross-links.
23.
24.

25. Glucose / galactose / fructose.
26. Glycerol; **two** fatty acid chains; one phosphate group.
27. It has one or more double bonds.
28.

Self-Test Quiz

1. Which line in the table is correct?

	Monosaccharide	Disaccharide	Polysaccharide
a.	galactose	maltose	glycogen
b.	glucose	starch	galactose
c.	fructose	galactose	starch
d.	glucose	fructose	cellulose

2. The four most frequently occurring elements in organisms are:
   a. hydrogen, nitrogen, oxygen, sulphur,
   b. carbon, hydrogen, oxygen, nitrogen,
   c. carbon, nitrogen, oxygen, calcium,
   d. carbon, nitrogen, hydrogen, sodium.

3. Hydrogen bonding is:
   a. only found in water,
   b. an attraction between weak negative and positive charges,
   c. a bond between hydrogen atoms,
   d. formed during a condensation reaction.

4. Cohesion between water molecules means that:
   a. water is a good solvent,
   b. substances can diffuse in water,
   c. osmosis can occur within a cell,
   d. a transpiration stream can occur in plants.

5. Carbohydrates, lipids, proteins and nucleic acids **all** contain the elements:
   a. nitrogen and oxygen,
   b. carbon, hydrogen and nitrogen,
   c. hydrogen, carbon and oxygen,
   e. nitrogen, carbon and oxygen.

6. The term organic can be described as:
   a. the element carbon,
   b. a compound containing water,
   c. a compound containing carbon,
   d. a compound that dissolves in water.

7. Which one of the following represents the general structure of an amino acid?

a.

NH₂CHRCOOH
b.

NH₃CHRCOOH
c.

d.

8. Which of the following represents the basic structure of the sugar ribose?

a.

b.

c.

d.

IBSL Biology 2016 © Ashby Merson-Davies

9. How many covalent bonds can carbon form?
    a. 2,
    b. 4,
    c. 6,
    d. 8.

10. Adhesion only occurs:
    a. between different molecules,
    b. between carbon-containing molecules,
    c. between organic molecules,
    d. between water molecules.

11. Which line in the table shows the correct sugar used for the polysaccharide?

	Starch	Cellulose	Glycogen
a.	alpha-D-glucose	alpha-D-glucose	beta-D-glucose
b.	alpha-D-glucose	beta-D-glucose	alpha-D-glucose
c.	beta-D-glucose	alpha-D-glucose	alpha-D-glucose
d.	beta-D-glucose	alpha-D-glucose	beta-D-glucose

12. Which type of bond makes cellulose very strong?
    a. covalent,
    b. disulphide bridge,
    c. ionic,
    d. hydrogen.

13. Polymerisation occurs in carbohydrates due to:
    a. repeated condensation reactions,
    b. hydrogen bonding,
    c. bonding to proteins to form glycoproteins,
    d. repeated hydrolysis reactions.

14. Identify this molecular structure:
    a. steroid,
    b. fatty acid,
    c. amino acid,
    d. polysaccharide.

15. Which of the following is **not** a lipid?
    a. cholesterol,
    b. triglyceride,
    c. phospholipid,
    d. glycerol.

16. The number of carbon atoms in glycerol is:
    a. dependent upon the size of the fatty acids,
    b. n,
    c. 3,
    d. 6.

17. Which of the following shows the cis structure in a fatty acid?

a.   b.   c.   d.

18. Which of the following bonds does **not** occur in a saturated fatty acid?

$$C{=}O \qquad C{-}O \qquad C{=}C \qquad C{-}H$$

     a.   b.   c.   d.

19. Approximately how many kJ of energy per gram are released from lipids?
    a, 17,
    b. 38,
    c. 24,
    d. 54.

20. A person is 1.2m tall and has a body mass of 30kg. Their BMI is@
    a. 25 kg m^2,
    b. 0.04 kg m^2,
    c. 21 kg m^2,
    d. 40 kg m^2.

IBSL Biology 2016 © Ashby Merson-Davies

Molecular Biology Part 2
Amino acids, proteins, and nucleic acids

Proteins are the major structural molecules of animals. Proteins also form most enzymes which are the molecules that control and regulate metabolism. Nucleic acids contain the genetic code that is used to build an organism.

Amino acids

Key points
These are the building blocks of proteins.
The key characteristic is that they contain nitrogen in the amino group $-NH_2$.

Amino acid structure

$NH_2CHRCOOH$

Three different ways of writing the structure of an amino acid.

$NH_2 - CH - COOH$ (with R group)

Key points
A specific amino acid is determined by its **R** group.
The simplest R group is H giving the amino acid glycine – $NH_2\,CH_2\,COOH$.
R groups can be neutral, have a positive charge ($-NH_3^+$) or a negative charge ($-COO^-$).
These charged R groups are essential in holding the 3 dimensional structure together.
The charged R groups are affected by changes in pH – see page 37.

Are there only 20 amino acids?
Key points
There are 20 standard amino acids – see the codon table on page 42.
Two additional genetically coded amino acids have been discovered more recently.
They are pyrrolysine and selenocysteine – see blue box below.

Organisms can modify a '*standard*' amino acid in a polypeptide to make a different one.
This occurs as a post-translational modification – see yellow box below.
The purpose is to alter the function of the protein.

> There are 64 codons and they have all been assigned a function, either one of the 20 standard amino acids or a stop codon. How can these additional two amino acids be coded for?
> Pyrrolysine is found in methanogenic archaea (see pp. 156 & 199) and one known species of bacterium. These organisms use the UAG codon which in other organisms is a stop codon.
> Selenocysteine is widespread in both prokaryotes and eukaryotes. It uses the codon UGA which is also a stop codon, but where selenocysteine needs to be incorporated into the polypeptide the codon is 'recoded' using a special RNA molecule.

> There are many ways amino acids are modified after the polypeptide has been formed. One example is the modification of glutamine to pyroglutamate which commonly occurs in antibodies to make them more resistant to aminopeptidases. These enzymes are used to break down unwanted cellular proteins, especially during antigen processing.

Proteins

Key points
➢ Composed of linear sequence of amino acid residues – see page 24.
➢ Linked together by condensation – see page 24.
➢ Polypeptide formation occurs on the ribosomes during translation – see page 44.
➢ Most polypeptides are formed from the common 20 amino acids (but see above).
➢ These can be linked in any combination or number giving a huge range of polypeptides
➢ The sequence is coded for by the gene.
➢ The sequence determines the 3 dimensional conformation (shape) of the polypeptide due to interaction between the different R groups.
➢ A single chain of amino acids is a polypeptide but is often called a protein – see yellow box on next page.
➢ Every individual has a unique proteome – see green box on next page.

 IBSL Biology 2016 © Ashby Merson-Davies

Proteome

This is the set of expressed proteins in a particular cell or organism under a given set of environmental conditions.

The proteome is therefore unique to an individual and will change depending on what proteins the cell/organism requires. For example your proteome will be different when you have a cold compared to before you caught the virus.

The proteome shows what is actually happening compared to the genome which shows what could potentially happen.

Proteomics

This is the production of proteins by cells cultured in fermenters.

This offers many opportunities for the food, pharmaceutical, and other industries.

Difference between a polypeptide and a protein

A polypeptide is just a single linear sequence of amino acid residues.

A protein could also be the same or two or more polypeptide chains linked together.

Examples - myoglobin is a polypeptide,
        - haemoglobin is a protein consisting of four polypeptide chains.

Protein structure

Proteins can range from very simple molecules of just a few amino acids to huge molecules containing several polypeptide chains.

2.3 The 3D structure of the protease enzyme pepsin.

haem groups

2.4 The 3D structure of haemoglobin. This also has 4 polypeptide subunits.

Fibrous and globular proteins

Key points

Proteins are found in two forms – fibrous and globular.

The shape of the protein is closely linked to its function.

2.5 A blood clot showing red cells and platelets (white) trapped in a mesh of fibrin fibres.

Protein functions

Function	Example	Structure	Description
Defence	Immunoglobulins	Globular	These are antibodies produced by plasma cells (see page 122) and are used to destroy antigens.
Enzyme	Rubisco	Globular	This is one of hundreds of enzymes that catalyse the metabolic processes within organisms. Rubisco (full name ribulose bisphosphate carboxylase) is involved in photosynthesis.
Hormone	Insulin	Globular	This is one of many hormones. It is produced by the beta cells of the pancreas to reduce plasma glucose – see page 130.
Structural	Collagen.	Fibrous	A fibrous protein found in artery walls and tendons.
Trapping	Spider silk	Fibrous	This incredibly strong protein is used for capturing prey.
Light receptor	Rhodopsin	Globular, conjugated	This is found in the photoreceptor cells of the retina in the eye.
Transport	Haemoglobin	Globular, conjugated	This red coloured protein transports oxygen within the blood.
Pump	Na+/K+ ATPase	Globular	This is one example of an active transport pump for moving substances across a membrane against a concentration gradient. Present in neurons – see page 126.
Osmoregulation	Albumin	Globular	This is one of many plasma proteins that has an important role in controlling the water potential of the blood and in buffering the blood pH.

> The examples in black are the ones in the syllabus. Other interesting ones are in blue.

Denaturing of proteins by temperature and pH

Key points

➢ Many proteins are large molecules folded into a three-dimensional shape.
➢ This shape is held in place by a variety of bonds and these are strongest at the optimum pH and temperature.
➢ If these bonds are broken then the shape of the protein is changed and it loses its function.
➢ The protein has become denatured.
➢ Denaturing is especially significant with enzymes – see page 95.

1. Effect of temperature
   Key points
➢ At every temperature above absolute zero (0^0 Kelvin) atoms vibrate.
➢ As the temperature increases so does the amount of vibration.
➢ Eventually the movement of the atoms is so great that the weak bonds break and the protein structure begins to break down.

Physiological temperatures   Temperature

2.6 Albumen is the protein in egg white. It is normally a clear jelly but when heated it becomes a white solid.

2. Effect of pH
   Key points
   (Refer back to amino acid structure on page 34).
   ➢ Amino acids with opposite charges on their side groups can form an ionic bond.

2.7 Albumin solution before and after adding acid

➢ If the pH increases then there are fewer protons.
➢ Thus a proton dissociates from the NH_3^+ group leaving an NH_2 which breaks the ionic bond.

➢ If the pH decreases then there are more protons.
➢ A proton can associate with the COO- group forming COOH which breaks the ionic bond.

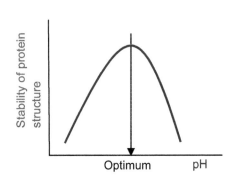

- Note the symmetry of the curve.

1. Draw the structure of an amino acid.

2. What is an amino group?

3. What is the key element that will allow you to recognise an amino acid?

4. Which component of an amino acid determines the type of amino acid?

5. How many amino acids are commonly used to make a polypeptide?

6. Give the names of two additional amino acids.

7. What determines the sequence of amino acid residues in a polypeptide?

8. Which part of the amino acid residue determines the 3D structure of a polypeptide?

9. State what a proteome is.

10. State five examples of the functions of proteins with a named example for each.

11. State the type of reaction used to build a polypeptide.

12. Where does polypeptide synthesis take place?

Nucleic acids
Key points
➢ There are two types – DNA (deoxyribonucleic acid) and RNA (ribonucleic acid).
➢ There are three types of RNA - mRNA (messenger) – see page 44,
  - tRNA (transfer) – see page 46,
  - rRNA (ribosomal)
➢ DNA and RNA are polymers of nucleotides.
➢ DNA is a double helix of two antiparallel strands of nucleotides linked by hydrogen bonding between complementary base pairs.

Differences between DNA and RNA

	DNA	RNA
Number of strands	**Double** stranded	**Single** stranded, but can fold back on itself to form double stranded regions.
Pentose sugar	**Deoxy**ribose	Ribose
Bases	Adenine, cytosine, guanine, **thymine**	Adenine, cytosine, guanine, **uracil**

Nucleotide structure
Key points
Three components: - pentose sugar, deoxyribose or ribose,
  - phosphate
  - base

There are five bases: - adenine A
  - cytosine C
  - guanine G
  - thymine T
  - uracil U

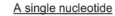

phosphate

sugar – in RNA it is ribose and in DNA it is deoxyribose

Draw

base

Strong covalent bonds link the sugar to the base and the phosphate

A single nucleotide

DNA structure

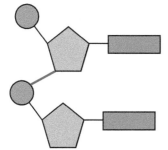

Two nucleotides are linked together by a covalent bond shown in red.

This is attached to carbon 3 of the upper sugar, and the phosphate which is attached to carbon 5 of the lower sugar.

This shows just one side, or strand, of the DNA double helix.

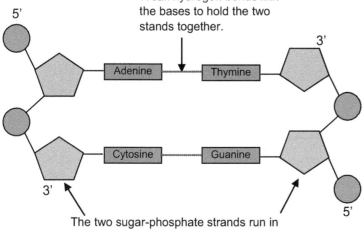

Weak hydrogen bonds link the bases to hold the two stands together.

Adenine — Thymine

Cytosine — Guanine

5'

3'

3'

5'

The two sugar-phosphate strands run in opposite directions – they are antiparallel.

The DNA double strand

Complementary base pairing
Key points
The bases always pair in a specific way. This is essential to ensure the two daughter molecules produced during replication are identical.
- adenine pairs with thymine   A – T
- cytosine pairs with guanine   C – G.

Use a simple idea to link the bases, eg Apple Tart and Chocolate Gateau, or A and T are 'straight' letters and C and G are 'curvy' letters.

Strand orientation
Each strand has a 5' or 5 prime end, and a 3' or 3 prime end.

These indicate the free ends where another nucleotide could be attached.

Nucleic acids always work in a 5' to 3' direction.

Francis Crick and James Watson deduced the structure of DNA in 1953 by collecting data from other scientists and making models.

These other scientists were:
Rosalind Franklin and Maurice Wilkins who produced very clear X-ray diffraction photographs of DNA. From these Crick and Watson determined that DNA was formed of two strands wound into a double helix and linked together by pairs of bases.

Erwin Chargaff who discovered that the numbers of adenine and thymine molecules in any given length of DNA were always equal, as was the number of cytosine and guanine molecules. This allowed Crick and Watson to deduce that adenine must be paired with thymine and cytosine must be paired with guanine.

DNA replication in prokaryotes

Key vocabulary
➤ Enzymes
  • Helicase
  • DNA polymerase
➤ Complementary base pairing

This key vocabulary is used in DNA replication, transcription and translation.

The simple double helical structure of DNA along with complementary base pairing suggested a mechanism for replication.

Enzyme	Function
Helicase	• Unwinds the DNA at the replication fork, • Breaks the hydrogen bonds between the bases, • Requires ATP.
DNA polymerase	• Adds nucleotides using complementary base pairing to the template strand.

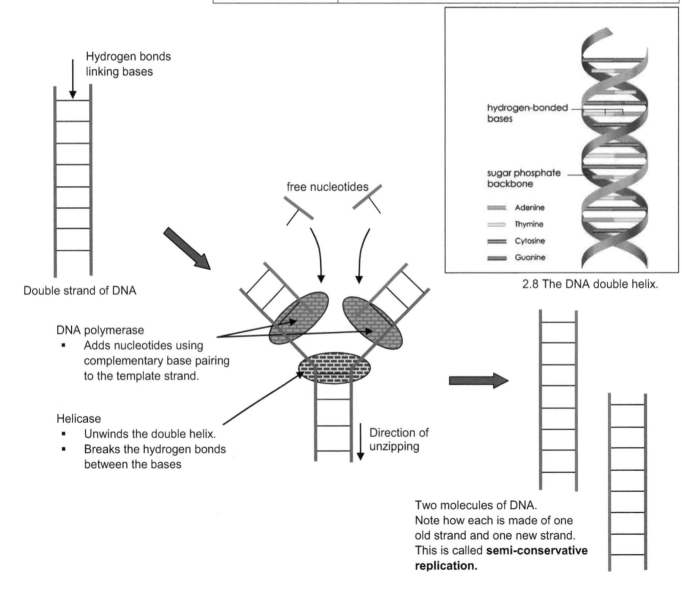

Hydrogen bonds linking bases

Double strand of DNA

DNA polymerase
▪ Adds nucleotides using complementary base pairing to the template strand.

Helicase
▪ Unwinds the double helix.
▪ Breaks the hydrogen bonds between the bases

free nucleotides

Direction of unzipping

hydrogen-bonded bases

sugar phosphate backbone

▬▬ Adenine
▭▭ Thymine
▬▬ Cytosine
▬▬ Guanine

2.8 The DNA double helix.

Two molecules of DNA. Note how each is made of one old strand and one new strand. This is called **semi-conservative replication.**

Meselson and Stahl
Proving semi-conservative replication of DNA
Key point

These two scientists set out to discover which of the two hypotheses about DNA replication was true – conservative or semi-conservative.

Bacteria are cultured in a medium containing normal nitrogen ^{14}N, The DNA is collected and centrifuged in a special fluid, It forms a precise band in the centrifuge tube.	The bacteria are now cultured for several hours in a medium containing heavy nitrogen ^{15}N, The DNA is again centrifuged this time the band is much lower.	The bacteria from the ^{15}N culture are transferred to a medium containing normal nitrogen ^{14}N, After each division of the bacteria (roughly 20 minutes) some bacteria were collected, The DNA from all the samples was centrifuged and this time the band was midway.

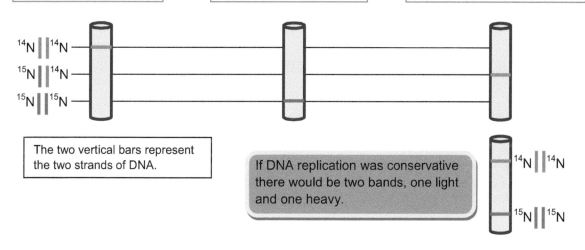

^{14}N | | ^{14}N

^{15}N | | ^{14}N

^{15}N | | ^{15}N

The two vertical bars represent the two strands of DNA.

If DNA replication was conservative there would be two bands, one light and one heavy.

^{14}N | | ^{14}N

^{15}N | | ^{15}N

13. List the components of a DNA nucleotide.	14. Explain fully what is meant by complementary base pairing.	15. Draw and label a nucleotide.
16. What type of bond joins the components of a nucleotide?		
17. The two DNA strands are antiparallel. What does this mean?	18. Name the building blocks used to synthesise DNA.	19. Name the region on the DNA molecule where helicase is acting.
20. List the enzymes involved in DNA replication.	21. What is the name given to the DNA strand that is being copied?	

Transcription

Key point
➢ This is the formation of a molecule of RNA from a DNA template in the nucleus.
➢ After the RNA molecule has been synthesised it leaves the nucleus via a nuclear pore.

Key vocabulary
➢ Enzyme – RNA polymerase
➢ Complementary base pairing

Key points
➢ The enzyme RNA polymerase has several functions:
  - It unwinds the DNA the helix.
  - It breaks the hydrogen bonds between the bases.
  - It builds the RNA strand using
    - RNA nucleotides,
    - complementary base pairing to the DNA template.
  - It rejoins and rewinds the DNA.

The mRNA codon table

Key points
The amino acids are in groups.
In general it is the first two bases that are critical, e.g. GG = glycine.
Only two amino acids have a single codon – methionine and tryptophan.
Methionine is the start codon in prokaryotes.

> You need to know how to use the codon table.

		Second letter								
		U		**C**		**A**		**G**		
First letter	**U**	UUU	Phenyl-alanine	UCU	Serine	UAU	Tyrosine	UGU	Cysteine	**U**
		UUC		UCC		UAC		UGC		**C**
		UUA	Leucine	UCA		**UAA**	*Stop codon*	**UGA**	*Stop codon*	**A**
		UUG		UCG		**UAG**	*Stop codon*	UGG	Tryptophan	**G**
	C	CUU	Leucine	CCU	Proline	CAU	Histidine	CGU	Arginine	**U**
		CUC		CCC		CAC		CGC		**C**
		CUA		CCA		CAA	Glutamine	CGA		**A**
		CUG		CCG		CAG		CGG		**G**
	A	AUU	Iso-leucine	ACU	Threonine	AAU	Asparagine	AGU	Serine	**U**
		AUC		ACC		AAC		AGC		**C**
		AUA		ACA		AAA	Lysine	AGA	Arginine	**A**
		AUG	Methionine	ACG		AAG		AGG		**G**
	G	GUU	Valine	GCU	Alanine	GAU	Aspartic acid	GGU	Glycine	**U**
		GUC		GCC		GAC		GGC		**C**
		GUA		GCA		GAA	Glutamic acid	GGA		**A**
		GUG		GCG		GAG		GGG		**G**

(Third letter column on right side)

It is useful to remember these two shaded ones, start AUG and stop UAG – A is the start of the alphabet and then simply change AU to UA for the stop.

IBSL Biology 2016 © Ashby Merson-Davies

22. State the functions of helicase.

23. State the functions of DNA polymerase.

24. Describe briefly Meselson and Stahl's investigation.

25. Name the enzyme involved in transcription.

26. List three functions of this enzyme.

27. Name the building blocks used to synthesise the RNA strand.

28. Which base on the RNA strand pairs with adenine on the DNA strand?

29. What is a DNA template?

30. How many bases form a codon?

31. Use the codon table on page 42 to determine which amino acid has three codons.

32. Use the codon table on page 42 to determine the amino acid for the DNA sequence ACA.

Translation in prokaryotes

Key point
This is the formation of a polypeptide from a messenger RNA molecule.

How can you stop getting muddled up between transcription and translation?
Think of language. Think of DNA as a 'language' of nucleotides, and protein as a 'language' of amino acids.

Transcribe means to copy in the **same** language. Thus in transcription you go from the **nucleotide** 'language' of DNA to the **nucleotide** 'language' of mRNA.

Translate means to change into a different language. Thus in translation you go from the **nucleotide** 'language' of mRNA to the **amino acid** 'language' of a polypeptide.

Remember also that '**c**' comes before '**l**' in the alphabet.

Sequence of nucleotides	Transcription	Sequence of nucleotides	Translation	Sequence of amino acids
DNA		mRNA		Polypeptide

Key vocabulary
- ➢ Complementary base pairing,
- ➢ Ribosome,
- ➢ mRNA,
- ➢ tRNA,
- ➢ Start codon
- ➢ Stop codon
- ➢ Peptide bond
- ➢ Polypeptide

A simple representation of a tRNA molecule with an amino acid attached.

Amino acid

tRNA and its anticodon

Key steps
These are illustrated on the next page. Remember that ribosomes may be free in the cytoplasm or attached to endoplasmic reticulum forming rER.

1. mRNA moves from nucleus and attaches to ribosome in cytoplasm.
2. First tRNA with amino acid joins to first codon by base pairing codon and anticodon.
3. Second tRNA with amino acid joins to second codon by base pairing codon and anticodon.
4. The two amino acids are now alongside each other and a peptide bond forms between them.
5. Ribosome shifts along one mRNA triplet or codon.
6. In comes the third tRNA and step 4 is repeated.
7. Steps 5 and 6 now keep repeating until the stop codon is reached.
8. mRNA and ribosome separate and the completed polypeptide breaks free.

Tip: Use simple codons such as CCC or AAA – much easier to base pair and less likely to make mistakes. Always, though, include adenine A so you can show it pairs with uracil U.

The start codon is AUG and a stop codon UAG. It is good to remember these but you do not have to – you can use any triplet.

1. mRNA moves from nucleus and attaches to ribosome in cytoplasm at the start codon.
2. First tRNA with amino acid joins to start codon AUG by complementary base pairing codon and anticodon.
3. Second tRNA with amino acid joins to second codon by complementary base pairing codon and anticodon.

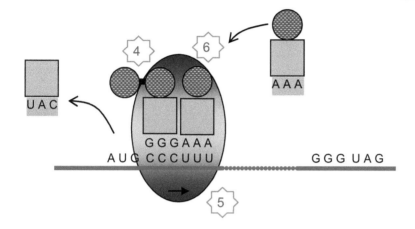

4. The two amino acids are now alongside each other and a peptide bond forms between them.
5. Ribosome shifts along one mRNA triplet and first tRNA is released.
6. In comes the third tRNA and step 4 is repeated.

7. Steps 5 and 6 now keep repeating until the stop codon UAG is reached.

8. mRNA and ribosome separate and the completed polypeptide breaks free.

If the polypeptide is going to be secreted or packed into lysosomes it is synthesised on the rER.

If the polypeptide is going to be used within the cell it is synthesised on the free ribosomes.

The polymerase chain reaction – PCR

Key facts

The polymerase chain reaction (PCR) copies and amplifies minute quantities of nucleic acid.

It is used in many situations such as forensic analysis and archaeological investigations.

The polymerase used is Taq DNA polymerase because it is heat stable.

DNA heated to separate strands

DNA polymerase and dNTPs added to build new strand

One cycle takes a few minutes

Process repeated

Taq DNA polymerase is a heat stable enzyme that was isolated from the thermophilic bacterium *Thermus aquaticus*.

Taq DNA polymerase is not good at replicating the DNA as it makes many mistakes because it does not have a proofreading function. It has now largely been replaced by another heat stable enzyme (again from a thermophilic bacterium) called Pfu DNA polymerase.

DNA profiling

Principles

➢ There are short sequences of DNA repeated many times.
➢ These sequences do not code for polypeptides.
➢ They vary between individuals so much that the probability of two individuals being the same is zero.
➢ PCR may be used to increase the amount of DNA.
➢ Great care to prevent contamination is required as the PCR will also amplify contaminant DNA.
➢ The DNA is cut up with restriction endonucleases – see Gene transfer on page 172.
➢ Gel electrophoresis separates the DNA fragments.
➢ The banding patterns are compared.

Uses

➢ Paternity – sometimes a woman is unsure who the father might be, or the man disputes being the father or wants to know if he is the father.
  ▪ DNA profiling from a mouth swab is used.
➢ Forensic investigations – often tiny samples of DNA can be found such as a drop of blood or saliva, a hair follicle, scrapings under a finger nail, and the DNA can be amplified using the PCR before profiling.

Other uses

➢ Family relationships for immigrants.
➢ Determining if rare birds and other animals being sold as captive bred have actually been captive bred or been stolen from the wild.

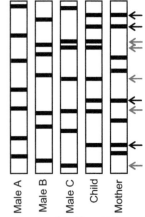

The black arrows correspond to the mother. The red arrows show that the father of the child is male C.

<u>An example of how DNA profiling has been used to determine paternity</u>

33. Name the triplet of bases on a tRNA that pair up with mRNA.	34. State the triplet of bases that would pair with the mRNA triplet AUG.	35. Name the bond that is formed between amino acids.
36. Where are polypeptides in secretory vesicles synthesised?	37. Which ribosomes would be used to synthesise RNA polymerase?	38. What does the polymerase chain reaction do?
39. Name the enzyme used in the PCR.	40. Why is this enzyme significant?	41. Name the building units used by the enzyme.
42. State two uses for the PCR.	43. Name the enzyme used in DNA profiling that is used to cut the DNA.	44. State two use of DNA profiling.
45. List the enzymes required for gene transfer.	46. Which of these enzymes is used to join pieces of DNA?	47. Name the bacterial component that the gene being transferred is attached to.
48. What is a 'sticky end'?	49. In most cases genes can be transferred between species and the polypeptide produced is identical. Why is this?	

Glossary

GEL ELECTROPHORESIS	Using an electrical current in a gel to separate charged molecules in a mixture based on their charge and size.
SUPERNATANT	The fluid remaining on top after centrifuging a liquid containing suspended particles.

Answers to grey box questions.   **Any words underlined are required.**

1. NH$_2$CHRCOOH or NH$_2$CH^{R}COOH.   2.   NH$_2$.   3.   Nitrogen.
4. The R group.   5.   20.   6.   Selenocysteine; pyrrolysine.
7. The sequence of bases/codons in the DNA/gene.
8. The R group.
9. The set of expressed proteins in a particular cell or organism (under a given set of environmental conditions).
10. Defence – immunoglobulins; enzyme – rubisco; support – collagen; hormone – insulin; light receptor – rhodopsin; trapping – spider silk, or any others from the table on page 36.   11.   Condensation.
12. Ribosomes.
13. <u>deoxyribose</u>, phosphate, base.   14.   Bases are paired in a specific pattern – <u>adenine with thymine and cytosine with guanine.</u>
15.

16. Covalent.
17. The deoxyribose – phosphate strands run in opposite directions.
18. DNA nucleotides.
19. Replication fork.
20. DNA polymerase.
21. Template strand.
22. Unwind the double helix; separate the DNA strands.
23. Builds the new DNA strand; using nucleotides; and complementary base pairing to the template strand.
24. Cultured bacteria with 14N and heavy nitrogen 15N, then back to 14N;
    Centrifuged and measured position of bands of DNA;
    Found intermediate band proving semiconservative replication.
25. RNA polymerase.
26. Unwinds the DNA helix; breaks the hydrogen bonds between bases; builds RNA strands; rejoins and rewinds DNA strands.
27. RNA nucleotides.
28. Uracil.
29. The strand of DNA that is being copied.
30. Three.
31. Iso-Leucine.
32. Cysteine.
33. Anticodon.
34. UAC.
35. Peptide.
36. Rough endoplasmic reticulum / rER.
37. Free ribosomes.
38. Multiplies minute quantities of DNA.
39. Taq DNA polymerase.
40. It is able to catalyse polymerisation at the high temperatures required for the process.
41. DNA nucleotides.
42. Amplify small amounts of DNA for forensic or archaeological investigations.
43. Restriction endonuclease.
44. Paternity test; forensic investigations; archaeological investigations; testing rare animals being sold to ensure they are captive bred and not from the wild.
45. Reverse transcriptase; DNA polymerase; restriction endonuclease; DNA ligase.
46. DNA ligase.
47. Plasmid.
48. A short section at the end of a DNA that is unpaired.
49. The genetic code is universal.

Self-Test Quiz

1. Identify this molecule.
    a. steroid,
    b. saturated fatty acid,
    c. amino acid,
    d. unsaturated fatty acid,

2. Which of the following diagrams represents a peptide bond?

    a. $-CHR-C \overset{O}{=} \quad \overset{H}{\diagdown} N-CHR-$

    b. $-CHR=C \overset{H}{\diagup} \quad \overset{OH}{\diagdown} N-CHR-$

    c. $-CHR-C \overset{R}{=} \quad \overset{H}{\diagdown} N-CHR-$

    d. $-CHR-C \overset{NH}{=} \quad \overset{H}{\diagdown} N-CHR-$

3. A polypeptide can be made up from which of the following number of different amino acids?
    a. 10,
    b. 20,
    c. 61,
    d. 64.

IBSL Biology 2016 © Ashby Merson-Davies

4. A proteome can be described as:
    a. a set of proteins,
    b. the proteins produced by a species,
    c. all the proteins produced by a gene,
    d. the set of proteins produced by a genome.

5. Denaturing of a protein occurs
    a. when bonds holding the structure together are broken,
    b. only when molecular movement causes hydrogen bonds to break,
    c. only when changes in pH cause ionic bonds to break,
    d. only when the disulphide bridges of the tertiary structure break.

6. The function of the active site of an enzyme is to:
    a. bind the products so substrates can form,
    b. bind the substrates in the correct orientation for catalysis to occur,
    c. prevent substrates from moving in the cytoplasm,
    d. unfold protein substrates so catalysis can occur.

7. Which of the following graphs represents the effect of substrate concentration on an enzyme controlled reaction with a fixed amount of enzyme?

a.

b.

c.

d.

8. Which of the following graphs represents the effect of pH on an enzyme controlled reaction?

a.

b.

c.

d.

9. Denaturation can be defined as:
    a. breakdown of a protein into its amino acids,
    b. loss of the functional properties of a protein,
    c. failure of an enzyme to catalyse a reaction,
    d. loss of peptide bonds.

10. Which of the following statements describes an immobilised enzyme?
    a. The enzyme does not take part in the reaction.
    b. The enzyme is denatured before being added to the substrate.
    c. The enzyme is attached to an inert molecule to hold it in place.
    d. Only enzymes involved in hydrolysis reactions can be immobilised.

11. A molecule of DNA:
    a. is made up from two strands of nucleotides linked by covalent bonds,
    b. contains five different types of base,
    c. has the bases linked to sugar molecules via phosphate,
    d. differs from RNA because it contains the base thymine.

12. Which of the following represents a nucleotide?

a.   b.   c.   d.

13. In the process of transcription which of the following enzymes unwinds the DNA helix?
    a.   RNA polymerase
    b.   DNA polymerase
    c.   primase
    d.   helicase

14. Which of the following statements about transcription is correct?
    a.   The enzyme DNA polymerase is required.
    b.   Both rRNA and tRNA molecules are required.
    c.   It takes place in the nucleus.
    d.   It takes place in the cytoplasm.

15. Complementary base pairing occurs during the process of transcription. Which base in the RNA strand pairs with adenine in the DNA strand?
    a.   thymine
    b.   uracil,
    c.   guanine,
    d.   cytosine.

16. Which of the following DNA strands corresponds to the mRNA sequence AACGUAUUC?
    a.   AACGTATTC,
    b.   CTTATGCAA,
    c.   UUGCAUAAG,
    d.   TTGCATAAG.

17. Use the codon table on page 42 to determine which is the correct the amino acid from the DNA sequence CCG GAA CGA AGC GAC.
    a.   proline – glutamic acid – arginine – serine – aspartic acid,
    b.   proline – leucine – arginine – alanine – aspartic acid,
    c.   glycine – leucine – arginine – serine – leucine,
    d.   glycine – leucine – alanine – serine – leucine.

18. Which of the following statements about tRNA is true?
    a.   It has a sequence of three bases called a codon.
    b.   It is composed of two strands.
    c.   It has a sequence of three bases called an anticodon.
    d.   It has the ability to complementary base pair to DNA.

19. Which of the following enzymes is used in the polymerase chain reaction?
    a.   DNA polymerase,
    b.   RNA polymerase,
    c.   DNA
    d.   DNA ligase

Chapter Three
Cell Biology

Cells are the building blocks of life. The cell nucleus contains the genetic code in the form of DNA, and membranes have a key role, not only in surrounding the cytoplasm, but compartmentalising the cell. Cells can divide by mitosis and meiosis.

Cell theory

The cell theory states that:
- Cells are the smallest units of life.
- Living organisms are composed of one or more cells.
- Cells come from pre-existing cells.

Questioning the cell theory

Points for discussion
- A cell is a functional unit of cytoplasm surrounded by a membrane and containing genetic material.
- Most multicellular organisms do contain many cells that conform to this cell structure – liver, pancreas, nerve, leucocytes, palisade, epidermal, cortex.
- Many cells do not conform to this:
  - Striated muscle tissue does not have separate cells as the nuclei are spread around in a single mass of cytoplasm – multinucleate cytoplasm.
  - Aseptate fungal hyphae are the same.
  - Some giant algae, such as *Codium*, also have multinucleate cytoplasm.

3.1 Striated muscle showing multinucleate cytoplasm

3.2 Fungal hyphae

3.3 *Codium fragile* (Dead Man's Fingers), Massachusetts coast

- Further examples:
  - Many plant cells have holes in their walls called plasmodesmata. The plasma membranes and cytoplasm of adjacent cells are continuous through these holes. This makes some plant tissues similar to muscle tissue and fungi in that a single mass of cytoplasm has several nuclei.
  - Mature red blood cells in humans do not have a nucleus.
  - The water transport cells in plants (xylem) are dead and have lost their end walls.
  - The food transport cells in plants (phloem) have lost their nucleus and the cytoplasm is very changed.

plasmodesma

3.4 Epidermis cells from an onion

white cells with nucleus

red cells with no nucleus

3.5 Human blood cells

3.6 Human cheek cells

3.7 Red blood cells from a bird. Note the nuclei

Spontaneous generation – Pasteur's experiments (around 1850s)

Key points
➢ Pasteur boiled up a nutrient broth in a flask and left the flask open – Experiment 1.
   ▪ After a few days it had gone bad due to bacterial growth.
➢ He repeated the experiment but sealed the flask after heating – Experiment 2.
   ▪ The broth remained sterile.
➢ He repeated the experiment again using an open swan-necked flask – Experiment 3.
   ▪ The broth remained sterile.
➢ He then broke off the swan neck – Experiment 4.
   ▪ The broth went bad.

Deductions
➢ The sterile boiled broth cannot spontaneously produce life.
➢ The bacteria that caused the broth to go bad could enter an open flask only if they could fall in directly.
➢ The bacteria could not enter through the open swan neck.

| Experiment 1 Nutrient broth goes bad. | Experiment 2 Nutrient broth remains sterile. | Experiment 3 Nutrient broth remains sterile. | Experiment 4 Nutrient broth goes bad. |

Surface area to volume ratio

Principle
➢ As an organism increases in size its surface area to volume ratio decreases.

This can easily be seen by comparing the following cubes.

Dimensions	1×1×1
Surface area	6cm²
Volume	1cm³
SA :V ratio	6 : 1

Dimensions	2×2×2
Surface area	24cm²
Volume	8cm³
SA :V ratio	3 : 1

Dimensions	3×3×3
Surface area	54cm²
Volume	27cm³
SA :V ratio	2 : 1

Key points
➢ The metabolism of a cell is linked to its mass : volume ratio.
➢ The surface area provides the exchange surface for heat and substances.
➢ The more cytoplasm the more heat and waste products generated, and the greater the demand for oxygen and nutrients.
➢ The models above show that the relative surface area decreases as the cube gets bigger.
➢ Thus organisms and cells develop strategies to cope with this problem. Examples are:
   ▪ Plant cells develop a large central vacuole,
   ▪ Intestinal cells and proximal convoluted tubule cells have microvilli,
   ▪ Leaf palisade cells are column shaped.

1. What does the cell theory state?	2. Describe one tissue or organism that does not follow the cell theory.
3. Describe simply Pasteur's experiment.	4. What was the essential point shown by Pasteur's experiment?

Functions of life

- **Metabolism** – all the chemical pathways that take place in the cell to build up molecules (anabolism) or break down molecules (catabolism).
- **Response** – reactions given to stimuli to help survival.
- **Homeostasis** – maintaining a constant internal environment.
- **Growth** – increasing the cell size or number of cells.
- **Reproduction** – producing offspring, either asexual or sexual.
- **Nutrition** – taking in nutrients for growth and energy.
- **Excretion** – removal of the waste products of metabolism.

Chlorella – a unicellular alga

- metabolism – respires, photosynthesises, synthesises protein, synthesises nucleic acids.
- growth – after dividing they grow by increasing the volume of cytoplasm.
- reproduction – divide into two, this is called binary fission, it is asexual reproduction.
- excretion – removes excess carbon dioxide by diffusion over the cell surface.

3.8a Chlorella

Paramecium – a unicellular organism

- metabolism – respires, synthesises protein, synthesises nucleic acids.
- response – can follow a chemical gradient to find food, this is called chemotaxis.
- homeostasis – species living in fresh water can pump out excess water flowing in due to osmosis by using a special structure called a contractile vacuole.
- growth – after dividing they grow by increasing the volume of cytoplasm.
- reproduction – divide into two, this is called binary fission, it is asexual reproduction.
- nutrition – feeds by taking in particles of organic matter in the water.
- excretion – removes carbon dioxide by diffusion over the cell surface.

contractile vacuole

3.8b Paramecium

Cell differentiation
Key points
- ➤ This means to become different and therefore specialise in a particular function.
- ➤ Cells in a multicellular organism are produced by mitosis.
- ➤ Hence each cell has all the chromosomes and a complete genome.
- ➤ Most of these genes will be switched off as they will code for functions that the cell does not do, e.g. liver cells will have the genes for eye cells, stomach cells, brain cells etc. switched off.
- ➤ The genes that are switched on are those associated with 'house-keeping' such as respiration to keep the cell alive, plus those associated with its specialist function.
- ➤ Differentiation of groups of cells produces specialised tissues.

Emergent properties
Key points
- ➤ Only multicellular organisms show emergent properties.
- ➤ Emergent properties arise from the interaction of differentiated cells.
- ➤ Differentiated cells can group together to form tissues, tissues group to form organs, and organs group to form organ systems.
- ➤ These interactions result in the whole organism being better than the sum of its parts.

Example 1 – the lungs (see page 111)
- Type 1 pneumocytes are very thin and specialised for gas exchange.
- Type 2 pneumocytes produce a surfactant which stops the alveolar walls sticking together.
- Without the two cell types working together the lungs could not function efficiently.

Example 2 – temperature homeostasis
- Blood transports heat around the body,
- Sweat glands produce sweat,
- Heat from the blood is used to evaporate the sweat cooling the body,
- The animal can survive in hotter environments that would kill other organisms.

Stem cells

Stem cells
Stem cells are undifferentiated cells found in multicellular organisms that can differentiate into specialised cells and can divide by mitosis to produce more stem cells. In mammals there are two main types of stem cell: embryonic stem cells, which are isolated from the blastocyst*, and adult stem cells which are found in a variety of tissues such as bone marrow. Stem cells can also be taken from the umbilical cord blood just after birth.
Autologous harvesting means removing stem cells from the person in whom they are going to be used.

Stem cell potency
Potency specifies the level of ability to differentiate. The more cell types a cell can divide into the greater its potency. There are 5 categories – see Stem Cell Glossary on page 86.

*A blastocyst is the hollow ball of cells that implants into the uterus lining at the start of pregnancy.

Key points
- ➤ Stem cells are undifferentiated cells.
- ➤ There are several different categories.
- ➤ They retain the capacity to divide and to have the ability to differentiate along different pathways such as during embryonic development.
- ➤ Some tissues retain stem cells in order to continue producing new cells or to replace damaged cells.
- ➤ Some types of stem cell have the potential for therapeutic use – see boxes on next page.

Stargardt's disease – background
This is an inherited disease which results in a gradual loss, starting in early childhood, of the central area of vision. It can lead to complete blindness. It is caused by a recessive allele (see page 176) which destroys cells in the retinal pigment epithelium (RPE). These cells lie just underneath the layer of photoreceptor cells and maintain the functions of the photoreceptors. If the RPE cells cannot function the photoreceptor cells will degenerate and vision is lost.

Stargardt's disease
Key points
➢ Stem cell therapy is aimed at replacing the RPE cells – see lower blue box on the previous page.
➢ The work is at the clinical trial stage (2014–15).
➢ Human embryonic stem cells (ESCs) were induced to develop into RPE cells.
➢ These were injected directly into the affected area in the eye.
➢ Results from the trials showed that the cells survived and multiplied.
➢ This lead to some improvement in vision in the patients.

Leukemia
Key points
➢ Leukaemia is a cancer of white blood cells or leucocytes.
➢ Leucocytes are made in the bone marrow from multipotent adult stem cells.
➢ The leucocytes are released into the blood stream to fight off infection.
➢ Leukaemia is when these cells grow abnormally.
➢ Chemotherapy is used to kill all the bone marrow cells, the normal cells as well as the abnormal ones.
➢ Stem cells can be obtained from donor bone marrow or umbilical cord blood.
➢ These are introduced into the patient's blood and the stem cells migrate to the bone marrow and start to produce healthy leucocytes.

Ethics of the therapeutic uses of stem cells
Key points
❖ **Adult tissues**
➢ Autologous harvesting (see upper blue box on previous page) is the least controversial since the cells come from the patient and the person is not harmed.
➢ If harvested from the patient rejection problems do not occur as they are a perfect tissue match.
➢ They are less likely to develop malignant tumours compared to embryonic stem cells.
➢ In other cases the cells come from a donor who has made the decision to donate their cells. This is usually the situation with leukaemia – see purple box above.

❖ **Umbilical cord blood**
➢ After a baby is born the umbilical cord is clamped and cut close to the baby.
➢ Within the umbilical cord there is still a quantity of the baby's blood which contains blood stem cells.
➢ The blood is easily collected and no harm is done to either baby or mother.
➢ The blood can be frozen for long term storage.
➢ Stem cells are likely to be genetically different from the patient leading to rejection if not treated.

> Umbilical cord blood can be used to treat children with cancerous blood disorders such as leukaemia or certain genetic blood diseases such as Fanconi anaemia.

❖ **Embryonic stem cells**
➢ This is the most controversial.
➢ Embryonic stem cells (ESCs) are pluripotent (see the Stem cell glossary on page 86) and therefore have great potential for therapy.
➢ They will not have accumulated any mutations compared to adult cells.
➢ There is a risk of them developing into tumours.
➢ They are likely to be genetically different from the patient leading to rejection if not treated.
➢ During IVF treatment (see page 136) more embryos are produced than are used.
➢ Unused embryos could be used for another childless couple, for research, for ESCs, or destroyed.
➢ The embryos have been created in order to produce a baby.
➢ Many people feel destroying an embryo to collect ESCs is morally unacceptable.
➢ If though an embryo is created specifically using SCNT (somatic cell nuclear transfer – see page 175) as a source of ESCs then the ethical issues become even more complex. See blue box below.
➢ The controversy arises over whether the pre-14 day embryo has 'rights' with respect to life. (An embryo older than 14 days cannot be used).

> SCNT was the method developed by Dr Ian Wilmut and used to create Dolly the sheep – see page 175.

> Follow these links to read articles on the ethics of using embryonic stem cells:
> http://www.eurostemcell.org/factsheet/embyronic-stem-cell-research-ethical-dilemma
> http://www.eurostemcell.org/factsheet/origins-ethics-and-embryos-sources-human-embryonic-stem-cells

5. What happens to the surface area to volume ratio as a cell increases in size?

6. Give one example of how a cell can avoid this problem.

7. What is the function of the surface area of a cell?

8. State three sources where stem cells can be obtained.

9. List the 7 functions of life and state briefly what each one means.

10. State two significant features about stem cells that make them suitable for stem cell therapy.

11. State three points about how stem cells are used to treat Stargardts's disease.

Electron microscopes

Key points

➤ Electron microscopes have a much higher resolution than light microscopes.
➤ This means they can see very small objects such as cell organelles, membranes and viruses, and even large molecules.
➤ The images can only be in shades of grey.
➤ Images can though be artificially coloured to make parts more clear.
➤ The object has to be non-living.

3.10 Artificially coloured scanning electron micrograph of a leaf surface

Microscopes

There are two main types – light and electron.
There are two types of electron microscope:
• transmission,
• scanning.
Key features of light microscopes:
• low resolution,
• can observe colour,
• can observe living structures.
Key features of electron microscopes:
• high resolution,
• scanning em can observe in 3D.

3.9 A transmission electron microscope

Resolution

The resolving power of a microscope is the smallest distance between two objects so that they can be seen as two objects. This is determined by the wavelength of the beam being use to see the object – the shorter the wavelength the smaller the distance between the two objects. Electrons have a very much shorter wavelength compared to visible light.

Prokaryotic cells
Key points
- ➢ Prokaryotic cells are cells with a simple structure and no membrane bound nucleus.
- ➢ They do not have membrane bound organelles, i.e. they are without compartmentalisation.
- ➢ They divide by binary fission.

Ribosomes
There are two sizes called 70S and 80S. (You do not need to know what these mean.) Prokaryotic cells contain 70S ribosomes and eukaryotic cells contain 80S ribosomes. However mitochondria and chloroplasts contain 70S ribosomes suggesting their prokaryotic origin in evolution.

Draw

pili

cell wall
70S ribosomes
cytoplasm
plasmids
plasma membrane
nucleoid containing naked circular DNA
flagellum

Example – *Escherichia coli* or *E. coli*

3.11 Artificially coloured scanning electron micrograph of bacteria showing pili and flagellae

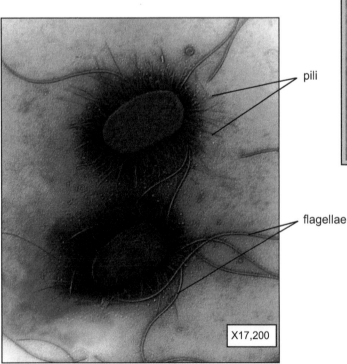

pili

flagellae

X17,200

3.13 *Escherichia coli* showing pili and flagellae.
Note the distinct difference in length and thickness

3.12 Streptococcus bacteria.
Note that these bacteria are round whereas *E. coli* is rod shaped

Electron micrographs of prokaryotic cells

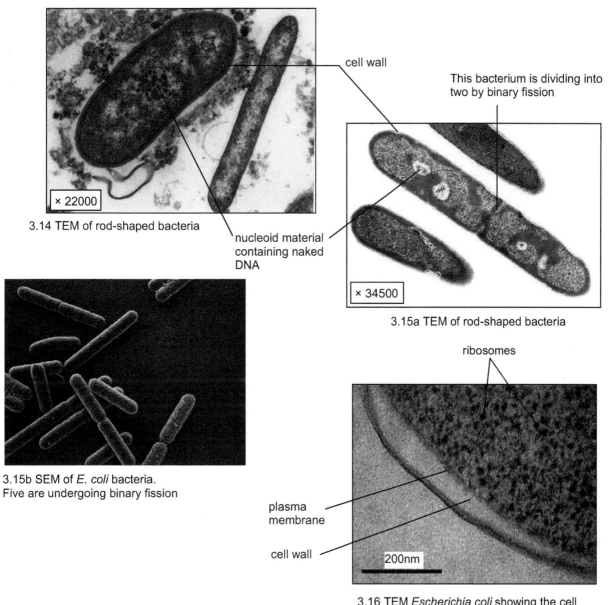

cell wall

3.14 TEM of rod-shaped bacteria

This bacterium is dividing into two by binary fission

× 22000

nucleoid material containing naked DNA

× 34500

3.15a TEM of rod-shaped bacteria

3.15b SEM of *E. coli* bacteria.
Five are undergoing binary fission

ribosomes

plasma membrane

cell wall

200nm

3.16 TEM *Escherichia coli* showing the cell wall, plasma membrane and ribosomes

12. What is the size of prokaryote ribosomes?	13. What is the name of the small circular pieces of DNA that are found in the cytoplasm of bacteria?
14. Distinguish between flagella and pili.	
	15. What is the name given to the type of bacterial cell division?
	16. Use the scale bar in the photograph above to determine the magnification.
17. State one advantage and one disadvantage of an electron microscope.	

Eukaryotic cells

Key points

➢ Eukaryotic cells contain membrane bound organelles, i.e. they are compartmentalised.
➢ Organelles carry out specific functions.

Animal cells

Key points

➢ Have centrioles.
➢ May have glycogen granules.
➢ May have phagocytic vesicles.

Structure	Function
80S ribosomes	Site of protein synthesis.
Secretory vesicle	Contains enzymes or hormones or neurotransmitter.
Lysosome	Store of hydrolysing enzymes that are released if the cell dies. Also used by phagocytes to digest ingested particles.
Phagocytic vesicle	Contains ingested particle, eg bacterium.
Rough endoplasmic reticulum (rER)	Transport and packing into vesicles of protein synthesised by the attached ribosomes.
Nucleus	Contains chromosomes that carry the genetic information.
Nuclear envelope	A double membrane with nuclear pores to allow exchange between cytoplasm and nucleoplasm.
Nuclear pore	Allows exchange of substances between the nucleoplasm and cytoplasm.
Centrioles	Involved in spindle fibre formation during cell division.
Golgi apparatus and vesicles	Modifies and repacks proteins from the rER into vesicles.
Mitochondrion	Site of oxidative or aerobic respiration.

You need to be able to interpret electron micrographs to identify organelles and deduce the function of specialised cells.
Examples.
- Large number of mitochondria – the cell is producing a lot of energy, perhaps for active transport.
- Large amount of rER – the cell is synthesising a lot of protein for export, perhaps digestive enzymes, or a hormone, or antibodies.
- Large number of vesicles – the cell is a secretory cell, again possibly producing digestive enzymes, or maybe they are neurosecretory vesicles.
- Large numbers of chloroplasts – photosynthesising cell such as a leaf palisade cell.

IBSL Biology 2016 © Ashby Merson-Davies

Electron micrographs of eukaryotic cells

plasma membrane

rough
endoplasmic
reticulum

nucleus

Golgi vesicles

mitochondria

secretory
vesicles

3.17 TEM of a pancreas acinar (exocrine) cell

× 18000

nucleus at interphase – the
chromosomes are not visible.

plasma membranes
of adjacent cells

nuclear envelope –
note that it is a
double membrane.

Golgi apparatus viewed from a
different angle and so not very
typical – look at the one on the
next page.

rough endoplasmic reticulum –
note the attached ribosomes giving
the membranes their rough
appearance.

mitochondria – note the double
membrane with the inner one
folded.

3.18 TEM of part of a eukaryotic cell

Here vesicles containing unprocessed proteins from the rER are joining on.

Note the vesicles budding off on both sides. These will either become lysosomes or they will be transporting processed proteins to the plasma membrane either for incorporation into the membrane (e.g. glycoproteins), or for exocytosis (e.g. hormones, digestive enzymes).

fat droplet – these usually stain black in electron micrographs.

× 28500

3.19a TEM showing a large and active Golgi apparatus

Golgi apparatus

cluster of free ribosomes

ribosomes on rER

Note the swollen end of the rER where a vesicle is forming.

Vesicles then move to, and fuse with, the Golgi apparatus.

× 85000

3.19b This shows the close relationship between rER and the Golgi apparatus

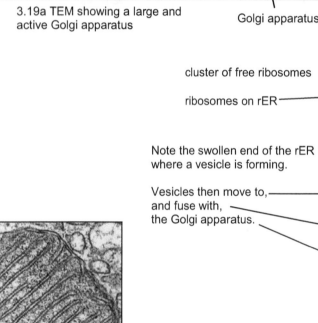

3.20 A mitochondrion. Note the cristae formed from the folded inner membrane

rough endoplasmic reticulum

plasma membranes of adjacent cells

mitochondria with cristae

3.21 TEM showing rER and mitochondria.
The black spot upper left is a lipid droplet.

Plant cells

Key points

➢ Have a cellulose cell wall.
➢ Mature cells may have a large central vacuole.
➢ Photosynthesising cells have chloroplasts.
➢ May have starch grains.

Structure	Function
80S ribosomes	Site of protein synthesis.
Rough endoplasmic reticulum (rER)	Transport and packing into vesicles of protein synthesised by the attached ribosomes.
Chloroplast	Site of photosynthesis.
Vacuole	Contains water, salts and waste products.
Nucleus	Contains chromosomes that carry the genetic information.
Nuclear envelope	A double membrane with nuclear pores to allow exchange between cytoplasm and nucleoplasm.
Nuclear pore	Allows exchange of substances between the nucleoplasm and cytoplasm.
Golgi apparatus and vesicles	Modifies and repacks proteins from the rER into vesicles.
Mitochondrion	Site of oxidative or aerobic respiration.

cytoplasm

cellulose cell wall

vacuole

chloroplasts

starch grain

nucleus

mitochondria

The nucleus appears to be very small. This is because only the end has been cut through.

3.22 A palisade mesophyll cell in a soy bean leaf

Comparing prokaryotic and eukaryotic cells

Prokaryotic Cell	Eukaryotic Cell
Naked DNA.	DNA wrapped around special proteins.
DNA in cytoplasm.	DNA enclosed by a nuclear envelope *.
DNA circular.	DNA linear.
No membrane bound structures.	Membrane bound structures such as mitochondria, endoplasmic reticulum and Golgi apparatus present which compartmentalise functions.
Plasmids present.	No plasmids.
Ribosomes smaller (70S).	Ribosomes larger (80S).

* Note – it is a nuclear **envelope** – there are 2 membranes.

Comparing plant and animal cells

Although both are eukaryotic cells they show some distinct differences.

Plant Cells	Animal Cells
Cellulose cell wall.	No cellulose cell wall.
Mature cells usually contain a large central vacuole	No large central vacuole but small vacuoles may be present in the cytoplasm.
No cholesterol in the plasma membrane.	Cholesterol in the plasma membrane.
No centrioles.	Centrioles present.
Store starch.	Store glycogen.
May contain chloroplasts.	Never contain chloroplasts.

18. What is the size of eukaryotic ribosomes?

20. State the storage carbohydrate in plant cells.

21. State the storage carbohydrate in animal cells.

22. Name three eukaryotic cell organelles that have a double membrane around them.

19. Complete the 9 shaded boxes below.

Feature	Prokaryotic cell	Eukaryotic cell
DNA	Enclosed in envelope or not enclosed?	Enclosed in envelope or not enclosed?
DNA	Naked.	
DNA	Circular or linear?	Circular or linear?
Mitochondria	Present or Absent?	Present or Absent?
Size of ribosomes		

23. What is the name given to this double membrane?

24. What does the term 'compartmentalisation' mean when applied to eukaryotic cells?

25. List four differences between plant and animal cells.

26. Animal cells – complete the 6 shaded boxes.

Structure	Function
Nucleus	
	Site of protein synthesis.
	Contains hydrolytic enzymes.
Golgi apparatus	
	Transport and packing into vesicles of newly synthesised protein.
Mitochondrion	

Membranes

Key points
➢ The cytoplasm of both prokaryotic and eukaryotic cells is surrounded by a membrane called the plasma membrane.
➢ Eukaryotic cells contain several membranous or membrane bound structures providing compartments.
➢ In eukaryotic cells the nucleus, mitochondria and chloroplasts are bound by two membranes.
➢ This double membrane is called an envelope.
➢ Membranes are partially permeable.

Membrane structure

Key components
➢ Phospholipids,
➢ Proteins,
➢ Cholesterol (animal cells only),
➢ Glycoproteins.

Phospholipids
Phospholipids have a hydrophilic head and 2 hydrophobic tails – see page 23.
This property is called amphipathic, thus they have to form a bilayer.

Proteins
These are highly variable in their structure, position and function. Some have a carbohydrate chain attached – these are glycoproteins.

Cholesterol
This is a characteristic of animal cell membranes.
It can comprise up to 50% of the membrane.
It reduces membrane fluidity by reducing the movement of the phospholipid tails.
It reduces permeability to some solutes.

Draw

glycoprotein

carbohydrate chain

protein

cholesterol

channel protein

Outer surface of a plasma membrane

phospholipid bilayer

10nm

peripheral protein

integral proteins

The fluid mosaic structure of membranes

Water based environment eg blood, tissue fluid, river

hydrophilic head

The more saturated the tails the less flexible the membrane – see page 22 for information about saturated and unsaturated fatty acids.

hydrophobic tails

hydrophilic head

Water based cytoplasm

integral glycoprotein

phospholipid bilayer

peripheral protein

integral proteins

3.23 3D drawing of the fluid mosaic model

The phospholipid bilayer

Key points
- Phospholipids are amphipathic – see page 23 for structure and properties of phospholipids.
- The phospholipids form a bilayer.
- There is always a water solution on each side of a membrane and so there must be a hydro**philic** part next to the solution.
- If there was only one phospholipid molecule then the hydrophobic tails would be next to water.
- The hydrophilic part will always want to remain in contact with the water solution due to the hydrogen bonds which form between the head and water molecules.
- The hydrophobic tails will want to remain in contact with each other due to the hydrophobic interactions and therefore form a lipid bilayer.
- The major force causing the formation of the bilayer is the hydrophobic interaction.
- Since the molecules are held together solely by forces of mutual attraction and not chemical bonds it allows the bilayer to be very flexible and to break and re-join easily – see page 71.
- The hydrophobic tails are flexible.
- Saturated fatty acid chains make a membrane less fluid because they pack more tightly – see page 27.
- Cholesterol makes some animal membranes less fluid by reducing the movement of the hydrophobic tails.

The proteins

Key points
- Position
  - Proteins on the surface are **peripheral** proteins.
  - Proteins partially embedded in the phospholipid bilayer or passing through it are **integral** proteins.
  - From above the proteins appear dotted around in the 'sea' of phospholipids looking like a mosaic.
- Structure
  - Some proteins on the outer surface are glycoproteins.
- Functions
  - Hormone receptor, ⎫
  - Active transport, ⎬ can be glycoproteins
  - Facilitated diffusion channel, ⎭
  - Electron carriers,
  - Immobilised enzymes,
  - Cell adhesion,
  - Cell-to-cell communication.

Models of membrane structure

❖ **Davson–Danielli model**
- The sandwich model – proposed in 1935.
- Phospholipid bilayer in the centre.
- Proteins coat both surfaces forming a protein – phospholipid – protein sandwich.
- Evidence for this came from electron micrographs done by Robertson in 1959 using a potassium permanganate stain which showed two dark lines with a pale line between.
- Danielli later added that protein lined channels passed through the phospholipid bilayer.
- Key problems with the Davson–Danielli model:
  - The proteins would be exposed to hydrophilic surfaces on both sides which is unstable.
  - Lipid soluble substances could not pass through.
  - Membranes around different organelles had different functions which would not be possible if all membranes had the same structure.
  - Membranes are bifacial, i.e. they have different inner and outer surfaces.

❖ **Singer–Nicholson model**
- The fluid mosaic model – proposed in 1972.
- It was supported by observations from the now more powerful electron microscope.
- Proteins were present on the surface of the phospholipid bilayer but not as a continuous layer.
- Other studies using dye marked proteins showed that these moved freely over the surface.
- Some proteins crossed the membrane from one side to the other.

27. What is a glycoprotein?

28. Distinguish between an integral membrane protein and a peripheral membrane protein.

29. What is the width of the phospholipid bilayer?

30. Which type of membrane protein forms channels?

31. Name the two molecules which reduce membrane fluidity.

32. Phospholipids are both hydrophobic and hydrophilic. What is the name given to this property?

33. Which part of a phospholipid is hydrophobic?

34. What is the major force causing the formation of the membrane bilayer?

35. Why do phospholipids have to form a bilayer in a membrane?

36. What is the property of a phospholipid bilayer that allows it to break and reform?

37. List 5 functions of membrane proteins.

38. Which type of eukaryotic cell does not have cholesterol as a membrane component?

39. Distinguish between the two models of membrane structure, naming both models.

Transmembrane transport

Simple diffusion
Key facts
- Many substances move through air and liquids such as cytoplasm, blood and tissue fluid by diffusion.
- Simple diffusion across the membrane is when substances such as oxygen, lipids and steroid hormones move through the phospholipid bilayer.
- Passive, therefore no energy from ATP is used.
- Particles are always moving in a random way.
- The substance always moves from a region of high concentration to a region of lower concentration using molecular kinetic energy.

Facilitated diffusion
Key facts
- Substances that cannot pass through the phospholipid bilayer have to pass through integral protein channels that have a hydrophilic core.
- This is called facilitated diffusion.
- The channels are specific and so have a binding site for the substance being transported.
- Sometimes these channels are gated to control the flow of the particular substance.
- Neurons contain both open and gated facilitated channels for potassium – see pages 128–9.

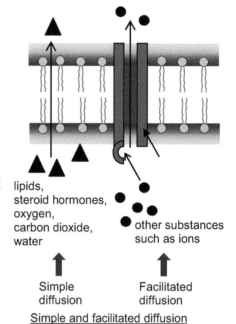

lipids, steroid hormones, oxygen, carbon dioxide, water

other substances such as ions

Simple diffusion

Facilitated diffusion

Simple and facilitated diffusion

edge of phospholipid bilayer

In these regions the chains of amino acid residues have formed helical shapes

3.24 The potassium channel

Osmosis
Key facts
- Diffusion of water.
- Passive, therefore no energy is used.
- The water always moves from a higher water potential (lower solute concentration) to a lower water potential (higher solute concentration).
- A membrane is essential.
- Water moves only by osmosis, **never** by active transport.
- Water can move by simple diffusion through the phospholipid bilayer due to its small size.
- Water can also move by facilitated diffusion through specific channels.

> Tissues and organs to be used in medical procedures must be bathed in a solution with the same osmolarity as the cytoplasm to prevent osmosis occurring which would damage the tissues.

Determining the osmolarity of a tissue
Key principles
- Cells placed in a hypertonic solution will lose water by osmosis and shrink.
- In plant cells the cytoplasm pulls away from the cell wall, a process called plasmolysis.
- Cells placed in a hypotonic solution will gain water by osmosis and swell.
- Animal cells may burst in a hypotonic solution (see blue box) but with plant cells the cellulose cell wall prevents this.
- Cells placed in an isotonic solution will remain unchanged as no osmosis takes place.

3.25a Rhubarb cells in distilled water

3.25b Plasmolysed rhubarb cells in a 5% sugar solution

> Some young people dancing in a hot night club have died as a result of drinking an excessive volume of water which has diluted the blood so much the red blood cells have burst.

Method
A tissue, such as fresh potato chips, is placed in a range of concentrations of salt or sugar solutions.

The dependent variable could be change in percentage mass or volume of the tissue, or change in volume of the solution.

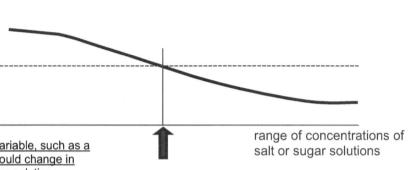

range of concentrations of salt or sugar solutions

<u>Graph illustrating how a dependent variable, such as a change in % mass of potato tissue, could change in varying concentrations of salt or sugar solutions</u>

➤ The osmolarity of the tissue is the concentration of the sugar or salt solution (blue arrow) where there is no change in the dependent variable.
➤ Water has neither entered nor left the tissue.
➤ The tissue cells are in osmotic equilibrium with the surrounding solution.
➤ The salt or sugar solution is isotonic to the cell cytoplasm.

Active transport
Key facts
➤ Always uses energy from ATP.
➤ ATP is hydrolysed to ADP + Pi.
➤ Transports against a concentration gradient.
➤ Requires an integral protein transporter in the membrane.
➤ Transport of substance requires a change in shape of the protein.
➤ The protein transporter has a specific binding site for the substance being transported.
➤ Some pumps transport two substances together, either in the same direction (symport) or in opposite directions (antiport). An example of a symport is the Na^+:Cl^- pump in the kidney. An example of an antiport is the Na^+:K^+ pump in neurons – see page 125.

3.26 Diagram of the neuron Na+/K+ pump in the neuron membrane.
There are two alpha, α, chains and two beta, β, chains.
The beta chains are glycoproteins.

Endocytosis

Key facts

- ➤ Endocytosis means taking substance into the cell.
- ➤ Phagocytosis takes in particles.
- ➤ Pinocytosis takes in solution.
- ➤ Energy from ATP is required.
- ➤ The plasma membrane folds inwards to form a vesicle which buds off.

> Endocytosis and exocytosis can occur due to the fluidity of the phospholipid bilayer.

Exocytosis

Key facts

- ➤ Exocytosis removes substances from the cell.
- ➤ This includes secretion of useful substances (enzymes, hormones, neurotransmitters), or excretion of waste.
- ➤ A vesicle in the cytoplasm joins to the plasma membrane and bursts.

> Take care to distinguish between secretion and excretion – see Glossary.

Transport vesicles

Key facts

- ➤ Vesicles bud off rER.
- ➤ Vesicles move through cytoplasm and join onto one side of the Golgi apparatus.
- ➤ Vesicles bud off other side of Golgi apparatus.
- ➤ Vesicle may move to plasma membrane for secretion of contents.
- ➤ Vesicle may remain in cytoplasm as a lysosome and fuse with a phagocytic vesicle.

Vesicle movement in cells

Here vesicles containing unprocessed proteins from the rER are joining on.

Note the vesicles budding off on both sides. These will either become lysosomes or they will be transporting processed proteins to the plasma membrane either for incorporation into the membrane (e.g. glycoproteins), or for exocytosis (e.g. hormones, digestive enzymes).

× 28500

3.27 TEM of a Golgi apparatus

Golgi apparatus

The origin of cells

Key points
➢ Cells can only be formed from pre-existing cells.
➢ The first cells must have arisen from non-living material.
➢ The origin of eukaryotic cells can be explained by the endosymbiotic theory.

The endosymbiotic theory
Points for discussion
➢ This theory is that eukaryotic cells arose from combinations of different types of prokaryotic cell.
➢ Usually, if one type of bacterial cell gets inside another, one of two things happens:
  • the host cell digests the invader,
  • the invader multiplies and kills the host cell.
➢ Thus, there is a battle between host and invader.
➢ The endosymbiotic theory imagines a drawn result – neither host nor invader wins and they settle down to work together.
➢ Suppose three types of imaginary prokaryotic cell which we will call 'Eater', 'Eliminator', and 'Sunshine':

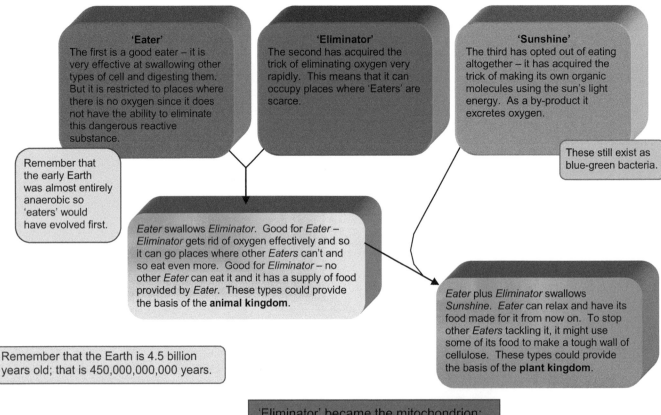

'Eater'
The first is a good eater – it is very effective at swallowing other types of cell and digesting them. But it is restricted to places where there is no oxygen since it does not have the ability to eliminate this dangerous reactive substance.

'Eliminator'
The second has acquired the trick of eliminating oxygen very rapidly. This means that it can occupy places where 'Eaters' are scarce.

'Sunshine'
The third has opted out of eating altogether – it has acquired the trick of making its own organic molecules using the sun's light energy. As a by-product it excretes oxygen.

These still exist as blue-green bacteria.

Remember that the early Earth was almost entirely anaerobic so 'eaters' would have evolved first.

Eater swallows *Eliminator*. Good for *Eater* – *Eliminator* gets rid of oxygen effectively and so it can go places where other *Eaters* can't and so eat even more. Good for *Eliminator* – no other *Eater* can eat it and it has a supply of food provided by *Eater*. These types could provide the basis of the **animal kingdom**.

Remember that the Earth is 4.5 billion years old; that is 450,000,000,000 years.

Eater plus *Eliminator* swallows *Sunshine*. *Eater* can relax and have its food made for it from now on. To stop other *Eaters* tackling it, it might use some of its food to make a tough wall of cellulose. These types could provide the basis of the **plant kingdom**.

'Eliminator' became the mitochondrion; 'Sunshine' became the chloroplast.

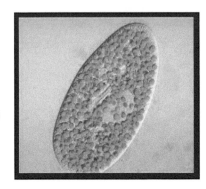

3.28 This photo is a Paramecium (a single celled organism) that has taken in Chlorella cells but not digested them. The Chlorella cells now provide sugars to the Paramecium. This is similar to the probable process that occurred in the evolution of the eukaryotic cell.

IBSL Biology 2016 © Ashby Merson-Davies

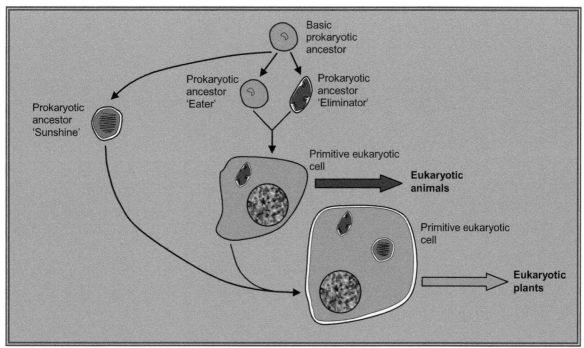

A possible origin for eukaryotic cells

Evidence for the endosymbiotic theory

➢ Chloroplasts and mitochondria both have envelopes (double membranes). The inner membrane would be that of the prokaryote that had been eaten, and the outer membrane would be formed around it from the plasma membrane of the eating prokaryote – see endocytosis – phagocytosis on page 71.

➢ Proteins on the outer membrane are largely produced by the cell DNA, whereas the proteins on the inner membrane are largely produced by the chloroplast / mitochondrial DNA.

➢ Chloroplasts and mitochondria have a loop of naked DNA as in prokaryotes.

➢ Chloroplasts and mitochondria can divide independently from the cell.

➢ When the eukaryotic cell divides there is a chance that the cytoplasm of the daughter cells will contain chloroplasts and / or mitochondria.

double membrane

➢ The ribosomes in chloroplasts and mitochondria are the same size as those in prokaryotes (70S), and smaller than those in eukaryote cytoplasm (80S).

➢ Thylakoids are similar to the structures found in blue-green bacteria.

➢ Chlorophyll a is the main photosynthetic pigment for both prokaryotes and eukaryotes.

➢ Mitochondrial cristae are similar to mesosomes, folded structures formed from the plasma membrane of prokaryotes and where respiration takes place.

➢ The 64 codons in the genetic code nearly always code for the same amino acid and the few exceptions have probably arisen since the common origin of life – see page 34.

Inner and outer membranes of chloroplast (left) and mitochondrion (right)

chloroplast thylakoids

mitochondrial cristae

3.29a Chloroplast membranes

3.29b Mitochondrial membranes

Note that the inner membrane of chloroplasts is not folded whereas the inner membrane of mitochondria is.

40. Distinguish between simple and facilitated diffusion.

41. What feature of a facilitated diffusion channel makes it selective?

42. How is a facilitated diffusion channel modified in order to control the flow of the substance through the channel?

43. State one example of a facilitated transport channel.

44. State four features about osmosis.

45. Which type of membrane protein is required for active transport?

46. Why is energy necessary for active transport?

47. State one example of an active transport pump.

48. Distinguish between endocytosis and exocytosis.

49. Which one requires energy?

50. State the two types of endocytosis and distinguish between them.

51. Name the cell organelle that produces the vesicles containing protein for export.

52. Name the cell organelle that synthesises proteins for export.

53. If the percentage change in mass of potato tissue is measured in solutions of different concentration and a graph plotted of this data, how is the osmolarity of the tissue determined from the graph?
Explain your reasoning.

54. Complete the 8 white boxes of key features for each of the three types of transport.

Diffusion	Osmosis	Active transport
With the concentration gradient.		
	Transports water.	
		Requires a membrane
	Does not require ATP.	

55. What is meant by the endosymbiotic theory?

56. State the two organelles that could have resulted from endosymbiosis.

57. State four pieces of evidence for the endosymbiotic theory.

Cell division

Key points
➢ **Cell** division is a process called cytokinesis.
➢ It is preceded by **nuclear** division, either mitosis or meiosis.
➢ Cyclins are involved in the control of the cell cycle.

> **Cyclins**
> The cell cycle is divided into three phases – interphase, mitosis, cytokinesis.
> Interphase is divided into three sub-phases.
> Each phase has to be regulated to ensure everything is ready before progression to the next phase.
> Regulation is carried out by enzymes called cyclin-dependent kinases, CDKs.
> CDKs are controlled by a group of non-enzyme proteins called cyclins.
> Each CDK has its own specific cyclin.
> The CDKs are present throughout the cell cycle but the specific cyclins are synthesised and broken down at specific points in each part of the cycle.

The cell cycle

Consists of:
- Interphase,
- Mitosis,
- Cytokinesis.

DNA replication occurs towards the end of interphase in preparation for mitosis.

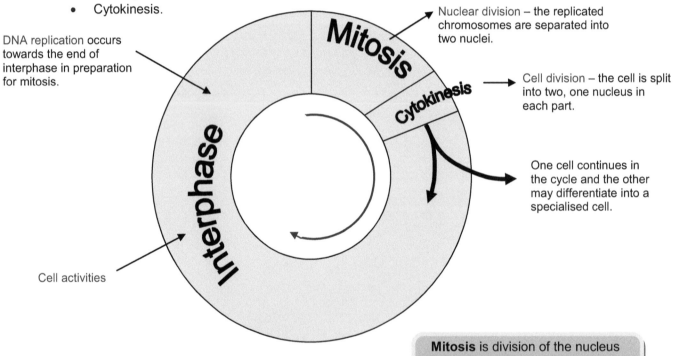

Nuclear division – the replicated chromosomes are separated into two nuclei.

Cell division – the cell is split into two, one nucleus in each part.

One cell continues in the cycle and the other may differentiate into a specialised cell.

Cell activities

Mitosis is division of the nucleus into two genetically identical daughter nuclei.

Interphase is an active period in the life of a cell when many cell activities occur, including transcription, translation, synthesis of other molecules, DNA replication and an increase in the number of mitochondria and chloroplasts.

Cytokinesis is division of the cell into two. The division may be equal or unequal.
Cytokinesis is different in plant and animal cells.

Mitosis is involved in:
♦ Asexual reproduction,
♦ Embryonic development,
♦ Growth,
♦ Tissue repair.

Mitosis

Phase	Key points
Prophase	• Replicated DNA condenses by supercoiling (multiple coiling) and becomes visible under the light microscope. • Spindle microtubules start to form. • Nuclear envelope breaks down.
Metaphase	• Microtubule network completed. • Microtubules attach to centromeres. • Chromosomes move to equator of cell.
Anaphase	• Centromeres split. • Microtubules contract. • Chromosomes pulled to opposite poles.
Telophase	• Chromosomes uncoil. • Microtubules break down. • Nuclear envelope reforms. (*This is effectively the opposite of prophase*)

> **Note:**
> **There are three key points for each phase.**

The difference between chromosome and chromatid

Prophase
Metaphase

Centromere

sister chromatids } chromosome

> **Note:**
> The two DNA molecules formed by replication are called sister chromatids until the centromere splits at the start of anaphase. After this they are individual chromosomes.

Anaphase

chromosome
chromosome

3.30 A human cell at metaphase. Chromosomes are blue, centromeres red and the spindle microtubules are green

Cell with one pair of chromosomes at interphase

Prophase
⇒ Replicated DNA condenses by supercoiling and becomes visible under the light microscope.
⇒ Spindle microtubules start to form (from centrioles in animal cells).
⇒ Nuclear envelope breaks down.

> Remember:
> **There are three key points for each phase.**

Metaphase
⇒ Microtubule network completed.
⇒ Microtubules attach to centromeres.
⇒ Chromosomes move to equator of cell.

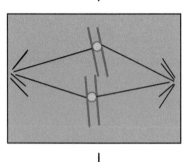

Anaphase
⇒ Centromeres split.
⇒ Microtubules contract.
⇒ Chromosomes pulled to opposite poles.

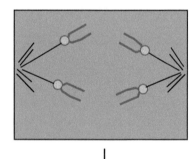

> A chromosome consists of a pair of sister chromatids, but as soon as the centromere splits the chromatids become chromosomes.

Telophase
⇒ Chromosomes uncoil.
⇒ Spindle microtubules break down.
⇒ Nuclear envelope reforms.

Cytokinesis

Two cells each with one pair of chromosomes.

early telophase – the chromosomes are still visible

later telophase – the nuclear envelope has reformed and the start of cytokinesis can be seen

cytokinesis continues – the developing cell wall is clearly visible

prophase – the nuclear envelope is still present

metaphase

anaphase

3.31 Mitosis in plant cells

Mitotic index
This gives an indication of the amount of mitotic activity in the tissue.
The calculation is:

number of cells at any phase of mitosis
total number of cells

The mitotic index is a way of measuring the dividing activity of a tissue. It is especially important in assessing the effectiveness of cancer chemotherapy. The index is determined before and during treatment. If it has fallen then that indicates the treatment is working.

★ cells in mitosis: 6

★ cells in interphase: 16

Index $\dfrac{6}{6 + 16}$ = 0.27

3.32 Calculating mitotic index

58. List the sequence of stages in the cell cycle.

59. In which phase of mitosis does the centromere split?

60. What structures attach to the centromere?

63. When does a chromatid become a chromosome?

62. In which phase of mitosis does the nuclear envelope break down?

61. Name the phase in the cell cycle when the cell divides into two.

65. In which phase of mitosis does the nuclear envelope reform?

64. List the sequence of phases in mitosis.

67. List four situations which involve mitosis.

66. Name the group of chemical substances involved in the control of the cell cycle.

68. Label the diagram.

Cell division and cancer

➤ Uncontrolled cell division results in a cancerous tumour.
➤ Tumours can spread via both blood and lymph.
➤ Mutagens, oncogenes and metastasis are involved in the development of primary and secondary tumours.

3.33 A typical appearance of nodulo-ulcerative BCC (basal cell carcinoma)

Mutagens

This is anything that causes a mutation of a cell's genome.
This could be by:

- directly affecting the structure of DNA such as a thymine dimer.
- affecting the replication of DNA.
- affecting nuclear division by damaging the microtubule mechanism or cyclin regulation.
- radiation in the electromagnetic spectrum of UV and above such as X-rays, gamma rays.
- a wide range of chemicals such as Aldrin, an organochlorine insecticide, and benzene, an industrial solvent.
- Reactive oxygen species (ROS), e.g. hydrogen peroxide. These are often natural by-products of metabolism in cells but are normally removed by the cellular antioxidants.
- Certain metals such as nickel.
- Certain viruses.

Metastasis

- The spread of cancer from one part of the body to another.
- A primary tumour develops in one part of the body but may remain there.
- It may though become metastatic where cells enter the blood or lymphatic system.
- These can lodge in another part of the body and form a secondary tumour.
- The secondary tumour has the same name as the primary, i.e. a primary tumour in the breast which spreads to the lungs is still called a breast cancer.

Oncogenes

- These are genes that, when mutated or expressed at high level, can turn a normal cell into a tumour cell.
- They are usually the genes involved in the control of the cell cycle.
- Cells that have been damaged in some way usually undergo programmed cell death called apoptosis.
- Oncogenes prevent cell death and allow the cell to survive and divide.
- Most oncogenes require an additional step such as a mutation in another gene or a viral infection to cause cancer.

The correlation between smoking and the incidence of cancer

➤ Smoking accounts for nearly one fifth of all cancer cases.
➤ Smoking causes more than four in five cases of lung cancer.
➤ Other cancers related to smoking include:

Tobacco smoke includes over 70 different carcinogenic (cancer causing) chemicals.

- mouth
- nose
- larynx

- oesophagus
- stomach
- bowel

- bladder
- kidney

- cervix
- ovary
- one type of breast

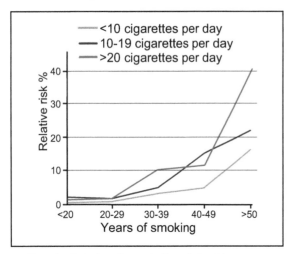

Graph showing the relative risk of lung cancer for men based on duration and intensity of smoking

Between 2005 and 2010, an average of 130,659 Americans (74,300 men and 56,359 women) died of smoking attributable lung cancer each year. Exposure to second-hand smoke causes approximately 7330 lung cancer deaths among non-smokers every year.
Non-smokers have a 20-30% greater chance of developing lung cancer if they are exposed to second-hand smoke at home or at work.

Meiosis

Key points
- ➤ Most cells are diploid, i.e. they have two sets of chromosomes in each cell nucleus.
- ➤ The chromosomes are in pairs.
- ➤ Each parent contributed one of the pair.
- ➤ A haploid cell only has only one set of chromosomes.
- ➤ Meiosis is a reduction division, i.e. halves the number of chromosomes from diploid to haploid.
- ➤ One parent nucleus results in 4 daughter nuclei.
- ➤ One or more of these nuclei differentiate into a gamete.
- ➤ Halving of the chromosome number allows for a sexual life cycle with fusion of gametes.
- ➤ It results in genetic variety.

> Since you have studied mitosis you already know most of meiosis. Meiosis has two phases, but the names are the same as in mitosis with I or II added. Likewise the key facts for each stage are very similar. On the diagrams the pattern is the same as in mitosis but the purple text indicates where the five differences are.

Phase	Key points
Prophase I	Replicated DNA starts to condense by supercoiling. Replicated chromosomes pair up in their homologous pairs to form a bivalent. (This is called synapsis.) Crossing over may occur between non-sister chromatids within the bivalent leading to exchange of genetic material. Supercoiling / condensation completed. Spindle microtubules start to form. Nuclear envelope breaks down.
Metaphase I	Microtubule network completed. Microtubules attach to centromeres. Bivalents move to equator. They align in a random way.
Anaphase I	Centromeres do **not** split. Microtubules contract. Homologous chromosomes pulled to opposite poles. The chromosome number is halved.
Telophase I	
Cytokinesis I	*First cell division starts.* These stages often merge with each other because they are opposite. The spindle fibre network breaks down and two new ones begin to form, often at right angles to the first one.
Prophase II	
Metaphase II	Microtubule network completed. Microtubules attach to centromeres. Chromosomes move to equator.
Anaphase II	Centromeres **do** split. Microtubules contract. Chromosomes pulled to opposite poles.
Telophase II	Chromosomes uncoil. Spindle fibre network breaks down. Nuclear envelope reforms.
Cytokinesis II	*Second cell division into four haploid cells.*

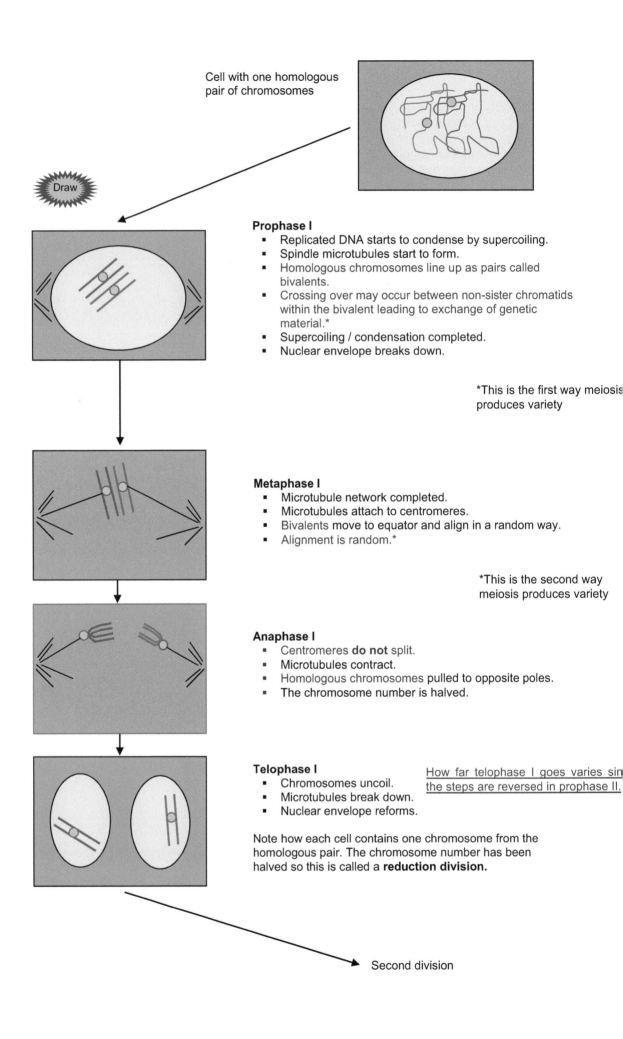

Cell with one homologous pair of chromosomes

Draw

Prophase I
- Replicated DNA starts to condense by supercoiling.
- Spindle microtubules start to form.
- Homologous chromosomes line up as pairs called bivalents.
- Crossing over may occur between non-sister chromatids within the bivalent leading to exchange of genetic material.*
- Supercoiling / condensation completed.
- Nuclear envelope breaks down.

*This is the first way meiosis produces variety

Metaphase I
- Microtubule network completed.
- Microtubules attach to centromeres.
- Bivalents move to equator and align in a random way.
- Alignment is random.*

*This is the second way meiosis produces variety

Anaphase I
- Centromeres **do not** split.
- Microtubules contract.
- Homologous chromosomes pulled to opposite poles.
- The chromosome number is halved.

Telophase I
- Chromosomes uncoil.
- Microtubules break down.
- Nuclear envelope reforms.

How far telophase I goes varies sin the steps are reversed in prophase II.

Note how each cell contains one chromosome from the homologous pair. The chromosome number has been halved so this is called a **reduction division.**

Second division

Cytokinesis I

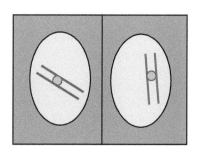

Each of these cells then undergoes the
second division of meiosis.
Only one is shown below for simplicity.
The second division is very similar to mitosis.

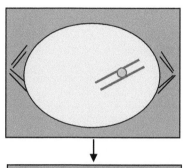

Prophase II
- Chromosomes undergo supercoiling.
- Microtubules start to form.
- Nuclear envelope breaks down.

> The amount of supercoiling
> required depends on how much
> they uncoiled during telophase I.

Metaphase II
- Microtubule network completed.
- Microtubules attach to centromeres.
- Chromosomes move to equator of cell.

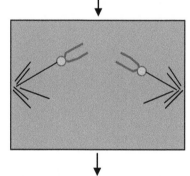

Anaphase II
- Centromeres **do** split.
- Microtubules contract.
- Chromosomes pulled to opposite poles.

> Remember – a chromosome
> consists of a pair of sister
> chromatids, but as soon as the
> centromere splits the chromatids
> become chromosomes – see
> page 77.

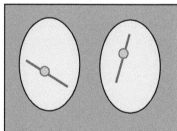

Telophase II
- Chromosomes uncoil.
- Microtubules break down.
- Nuclear envelope reforms.

Cytokinesis II in
both cells

- **Four** cells from one original cell, each with one chromosome
  from each homologous pair.
- These are **haploid** cells.
- One or more may now undergo differentiation into gametes.
- In spermatogenesis all four differentiate into sperms.
- In oogenesis only one differentiates into a mature egg.

Genetic variety

Key points

➢ Sexual reproduction allows for genetic variety.

➢ Meiosis produces variety in two ways:

  • Crossing over in prophase I resulting in exchange of maternal and paternal alleles between non-sister chromatids of homologous chromosomes.

  • Bivalents line up on equator in a random way in metaphase I – see diagram below.

➢ Variety is also produced by random fertilisation of gametes.

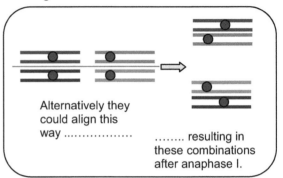

The bivalents may align this way on the equator .... resulting in these combinations after anaphase I.

Alternatively they could align this way .... resulting in these combinations after anaphase I.

How random alignment produces variety

Non-disjunction

Normally at meiosis the cell would split into four cells.

Key points

➢ Non-disjunction is when separation of homologous chromosomes or sister chromatids fails to occur.

➢ This can happen at anaphase of either the first or the second division.

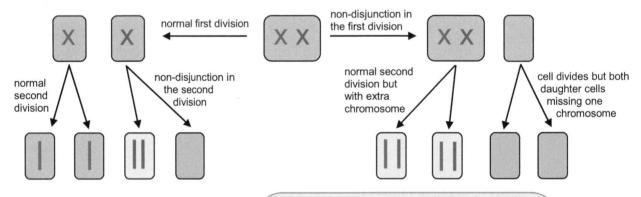

If a yellow gamete is fertilised then the zygote will have one extra chromosome.
An example in humans is Down syndrome where the extra chromosome is number 21. This is called trisomy 21.

If a brown gamete is fertilised then the zygote will be missing a chromosome. An example is Turner's syndrome which has a single X chromosome.

3.34 A woman with Down syndrome

Age and non-disjunction

Key points
➢ Studies have shown the significant association between advanced maternal age and chromosome 21 non-disjunction was restricted to meiotic errors in the egg.
➢ The association was not observed in sperm or in post-zygotic mitotic errors.
➢ Advanced maternal age was significantly associated with both meiosis I and meiosis II errors.
➢ Meiosis I errors were 8.5 times more likely in mothers 40 or more years old compared to mothers 20-24 years old.
➢ Meiosis II errors were 15 times more likely in mothers 40 or more years old compared to mothers 20-24 years old.

Karyotyping

 Pair of chromosomes showing matching banding pattern.

> Karyotyping is arranging the chromosomes according to their size and banding pattern to form a karyogram for that cell.

Key facts
➢ Used in pre-natal diagnosis of chromosome abnormalities.
➢ Observing major changes in chromosome structure due to mutations such as translocation or duplication.
➢ Observing changes in chromosome number as in Down syndrome.
➢ Foetal cells are collected using:
  • amniocentesis or
  • chorionic villus sampling.
➢ Risks – there is a small risk of injuring the fetus or causing a miscarriage.

The upper row is the standard banding pattern.

The lower row is a cut-out of the chromosomes from a photograph of prophase using the standard banding pattern to match the pairs.

A karyogram of a normal male

3.35 A karyogram of a person.
They are male – they have a Y chromosome.
They have Down syndrome – 3x chromosome 21.

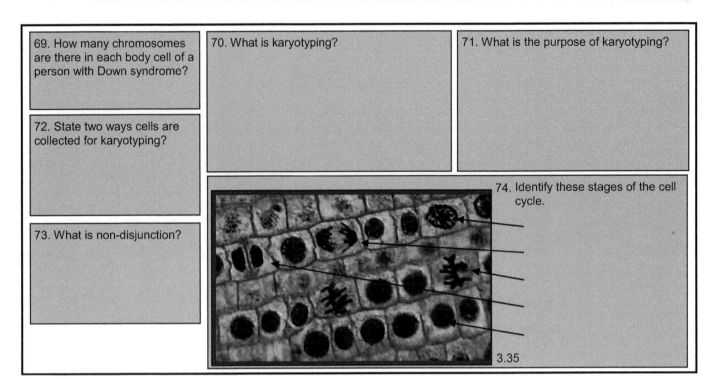

69. How many chromosomes are there in each body cell of a person with Down syndrome?	70. What is karyotyping?	71. What is the purpose of karyotyping?
72. State two ways cells are collected for karyotyping?		
73. What is non-disjunction?		74. Identify these stages of the cell cycle.

3.35

Glossary

ASEPTATE	A septum is a dividing wall: aseptate means without a septum.
CONTRACTILE VACUOLE	A special structure found in some simple fresh water organisms that collects the water entering the cell via osmosis and then pumps it out of the cell.
EXCRETION	Removal of the waste products of metabolism.
FACILITATE	To make easier.
GENOME	In prokaryotes it is all the information in the single circular chromosome plus plasmids. In eukaryotic animals it is all the information in a haploid set of chromosomes plus mitochondrial DNA. In eukaryotic plants it is all the information in a haploid set of chromosomes plus mitochondrial DNA plus chloroplast DNA.
HYDROPHILIC	Water loving.
HYDROPHOBIC	Water hating.
HYPERTONIC	A solution that has a higher solute concentration than the one it is being compared with.
HYPOTONIC	A solution that has a lower solute concentration than the one it is being compared with.
ISOTONIC	A solution that has the same solute concentration as the one it is being compared with.
KINETIC ENERGY	The energy an object possesses due to its motion.
MESOSOME	In prokaryotic cells the plasma membrane extends inwards to form a folded structure containing the enzymes for respiration.
OSMOLARITY	A measure of the concentration of osmotically active solutes in a solution.
PARTIALLY PERMEABLE	Some substances are able to diffuse through the membrane.
SECRETION	Release from a cell by exocytosis of a useful substance e.g. hormone.
SEM : TEM	Scanning electron micrograph : Transmission electron micrograph.
SOLUTE	A substance that dissolves in a solvent to form a solution.
SOLVENT	A liquid that dissolves a solute.
WATER POTENTIAL	The tendency of water to move from one region to another. The more dilute the solution the higher the water potential.

Stem cell glossary

TOTIPOTENT	Cells which can differentiate into all cell types because all their genes are functional. This can lead to development of a complete living organism.
PLURIPOTENT	Cells which can differentiate into nearly all cell types and arise from totipotent cells as a result of some genes being switched off. This makes them valuable for stem cell therapy. Read about how adult cells can be turned into pluripotent cells - induced pluripotent cells - by following this link. http://stemcells.nih.gov/info/basics/pages/basics10.aspx
MULTIPOTENT	Cells which can differentiate into a small range of closely related cell types. An example is haematopoietic stem cells (HSCs) found in bone marrow which can make every type of blood cell – red cells, white cells and platelets.
OLIGOPOTENT	Cells which can only differentiate into a few cell types.
UNIPOTENT	Cells which can produce only one cell type, their own, but have the property of being able to keep dividing which distinguishes them from non-stem cells. An example would be the germinal epithelial cells in the testis.

Answers to Grey Box Questions   Underlined words are required.

1. a. Cells are the smallest units of life. b. Living organisms are composed of one or more cells. c. Cells come from pre-existing cells.
2. See text page for 66 examples.
3. Boiled broth and sealed flask – broth remained sterile. Opened flask – broth went bad.
4. Life could not arise spontaneously.
5. Decreases.
6. Large central vacuole. microvilli. becoming columnar or flattened.
7. Act as an exchange surface between the cytoplasm and the cell's environment.
8. Adult tissues (e.g. bone marrow). Embryos. Umbilical cord blood.
9. See page 68.
10. They are able to differentiate into specialised cell types. They can continue to divide.
11. See page 70.   12. 70S.   13. Plasmids.
14. Flagella are long, attached at one end and few in number. Pili cover the surface and are short.
15. Binary fission.
16. 22mm = 22,000,000nm   22,000,000 ÷ 200 = 110,000× magnification.
17. See page 71.
18. 80S.
19. Not.   Enclosed.
    –   Attached to proteins.
    Circular.   Linear.
    Absent.   Present.
    70S.   80S.
20. Starch.   21. Glycogen.   22. Mitochondrion. Chloroplast. Nucleus.   23. Envelope.
24. The cell contains membrane bound structures that carry out specific functions.
25. See table on page 78.
26. Contains genetic material. Ribosomes. Lysosome. Modifies and packs proteins into vesicles. Rough endoplasmic reticulum. Release of energy through aerobic respiration.
27. Protein + carbohydrate.
28. Integral protein – partially or completely embedded in the membrane. Peripheral protein – on the surface of the phospholipid bilayer.
29. 10nm.   30. Integral.   31. Cholesterol. Saturated fatty acids.   32. Amphipathic.
33. Fatty acid chains.   34. Mutual attraction between the hydrophobic tails.
35. One end is hydrophilic and the other end hydrophobic. Each side of the membrane must be hydrophilic.
36. Its fluidity – there are no chemical bonds between the phospholipids.
37. See the list on page 81.
38. Plant.
39. Davson-Danielli model – sandwich, phospholipid bilayer between two layers of protein. Singer-Nicholson model – fluid mosaic, phospholipid bilayer with integral and peripheral proteins dotted around.
40. Simple – diffusion through the phospholipid bilayer. Facilitated – diffusion through specific integral channel proteins.
41. Specific binding site for the substance being transported.   42. Gated.
43. Sodium ion / potassium ion channel in neuron membrane.
44. Diffusion of water; with the concentration gradient; membrane required; no energy required / passive.
45. Integral.   46. Transport is against the concentration gradient.
47. Sodium – potassium pump in neuron membrane / sodium – potassium – chloride pump in kidney.
48. Endocytosis is taking substances into the cell; exocytosis is removing substances from the cell.
49. Endocytosis.
50. Pinocytosis – taking in water / solution. Phagocytosis – taking in particles.
51. Golgi apparatus.
52. Rough endoplasmic reticulum.
53. The osmolarity is the point where the change in mass is zero. This is because no water is entering or leaving the cell by osmosis – the external solution therefore has the same concentration as the cytoplasm.

54. Diffusion column – transports a range of substances; does not require a membrane; does not require ATP.
    Osmosis column – with the concentration gradient; requires a membrane.
    Active transport column – against the concentration gradient; transports a range of substances; Requires ATP.
55. Eukaryotic cells have evolved from ancestral prokaryotic cells that have joined together to co-operate.
56. Chloroplasts and mitochondria.
57. Chloroplasts and mitochondria have 70S ribosomes. These ribosomes synthesise several proteins used by the organelle. They have envelopes. They replicate themselves. They have their own ring of DNA.
58. Mitosis – cytokinesis – interphase. 59. Anaphase. 60. Spindle microtubules.
61. Cytokinesis. 62. Prophase. 63. When the centromere splits.
64. Prophase – metaphase – anaphase – telophase.
65. Telophase. 66. Cyclins.
67. Growth; asexual reproduction; tissue repair; embryonic development.
68. Sister chromatids. Chromosome. 69. 47.
70. Arranging photographs of the chromosomes in their pairs according to their size and banding pattern.
71. To look for abnormalities – prenatal diagnosis.
72. Amniocentesis. Chorionic villus sampling.
73. The failure of homologous chromosomes or sister chromatids to separate during anaphase I or II.

74.

Identify these stages of the cell cycle.

— prophase

— anaphase

— metaphase

— telophase + cytokinesis

— interphase

IBSL Biology 2016 © Ashby Merson-Davies

Self-test Quiz

1. The cell theory states that:
    a. living organisms are composed of cells,
    b. cells come from pre-existing cells,
    c. cells are the smallest unit of life,
    d. all of the above.

2. A description of emergent properties could include:
    a. cell growth is in an outward direction,
    b. germinating seeds emerge above the soil,
    c. stem cells emerge by differentiating into specialised cells,
    d. specialised groups of cells interact to form a functional unit better than the individual cells.

3. Which of the following best describes stem cells?
    a. They are cells found in the stems of plants.
    b. They are cells able to divide and differentiate along different pathways.
    c. They are cells that have differentiated into specialised tissues.
    d. They are cells that have had part of their genome switched off.

4. Which of the following statements about Stargardt's disease is correct?
    a. It is a disease of the eye which may be treatable with stem cell therapy.
    b. Stem cells can be used to replace damaged light receptor cells.
    c. Treatment requires the use of adult stem cells.
    d. Embryonic stem cells injected into the blood stream migrate to the eye.

5. Which of the following best describes the function of the Golgi apparatus?
    a. It synthesises the proteins used in lysosomes.
    b. It buds off vesicles which combine with the rough endoplasmic reticulum.
    c. Vesicles from the rough endoplasmic reticulum fuse with it.
    d. Vesicles released from the tips fuse with the nuclear envelope.

6. Which of the following statements about prokaryotic cells is correct?
    a. They can divide by binary fission.
    b. Meiosis is an important phase in their life cycle.
    c. They have fewer organelles than eukaryotic cells.
    d. They do not have a cell wall.

7. A characteristic of both prokaryotic and eukaryotic cells is:
    a. possession of a nucleus,
    b. compartmentalisation,
    c. ribosomes in the cytoplasm,
    d. presence of membranous cytoplasmic organelles.

8. In a prokaryotic cell:
    a. the ribosomes are found on the rough endoplasmic reticulum,
    b. the ribosomes are smaller than in the eukaryotic cell,
    c. the lysosomes contain digestive enzymes,
    d. the nucleus contains a single linear molecule of naked DNA.

9. The diagram below shows part of a cell membrane. Which molecule is an integral protein?
    a. One,
    b. Two ,
    c. Three,
    d. Four.

10. The main molecules forming membranes are:
    a. phospholipids and proteins,
    b. lipids and polysaccharides,
    c. carbohydrates and lipids,
    d. lipids.

11. The function of cholesterol in a membrane is to:
    a. make it more fatty,
    b. increase the hydrophobic property of the membrane,
    c. help to hold the peripheral proteins in place,
    d. reduce the permeability of the membrane to certain solutes.

12. The diagram below shows part of a cell membrane. Which molecule is a glycoprotein?
    a. One,
    b. Two,
    c. Three,
    d. Four.

13. Which of the following statements is correct?
    a. Active transport uses energy from ATP to transfer molecules across a membrane against a concentration gradient.
    b. Diffusion is the movement of water from a concentrated solution to a weak solution.
    c. Osmosis requires energy from ATP.
    d. Molecules can only diffuse across a membrane.

14. Which of the following statements is correct?
    a. A phospholipid has hydrophobic regions at both ends of the molecule.
    b. A membrane is made up of two layers of protein with a hydrophobic core.
    c. Proteins embedded in a membrane can act as transport channels.
    d. The presence of cholesterol in a membrane is harmful.

15. Which is the best description of vesicle movement within a cell?
    a. from the plasma membrane to the Golgi apparatus,
    b. from the Golgi apparatus to the rER,
    c. from the plasma membrane to the rER,
    d. from the rER to the Golgi apparatus.

16. Facilitated diffusion means:
    a. The transfer of substances through an integral protein channel in a membrane against a concentration gradient.
    b. Using ATP to facilitate the diffusion of substances from one part of a cell to another.
    c. Using a protein carrier and energy to diffuse substances rapidly down a concentration gradient.
    d. The diffusion of substances through an integral protein channel in a membrane.

17. As a cell increases in size:
    a. the surface area to volume ratio decreases,
    b. the surface area to volume ratio increases,
    c. the surface area to volume ratio does not change,
    d. the surface area to volume ratio begins to decrease only after the cell reaches a certain size.

18. If cells or tissues are going to be used in medical procedures then they must be bathed in a solution with the same osmolarity as the blood. This is:
    a. to allow osmosis to occur,
    b. to maintain the same ion concentrations in both cells and blood,
    c. to allow active transport of glucose and other nutrients into the cells,
    d. to prevent osmosis from occurring.

19. In an investigation, the osmolarity of the cells in a piece of potato tissue bathed in sucrose solutions of known concentration could be found when:
    a. the volume of the sucrose solution begins to decrease,
    b. when the mass of the potato tissue begins to decrease,
    c. when the mass of the potato tissue remains unchanged,
    d. the volume of the sucrose solution begins to increase.

20. In multicellular organisms cells differentiate because:
    a. some of their genes are expressed but not others,
    b. some genes are lost from the nucleus,
    c. not all genes are passed on when the cell reproduces,
    d. the nucleus is lost.

21. Which of the following statements is correct?
    a. Animal cells are round whereas plant cells are square.
    b. Plant cell walls are enclosed in membrane.
    c. Both plant and animal cells have 80S ribosomes.
    d. Animal cells contain more organelles than plant cells.

22. The data in the table below shows the normal concentration of two ions inside and outside the nerve cell of a squid.

Ions	Concentration / mmoles dm^{-3}	
	Inside	Outside
Potassium K$^+$	0.400	0.020
Chloride Cl$^-$	0.120	0.560

This information shows that:
    a. potassium ions diffuse into nerve cells whereas chloride ions diffuse out,
    b. osmosis creates diffusion gradients for these two ions,
    c. potassium ions are moved out of the cell by active transport whereas chloride ions are actively moved in,
    d. chloride ions are moved out of the cell by active transport whereas potassium ions are actively moved in.

23. Which of the following statements could be used as evidence for the endosymbiotic theory?
    a. Prokaryotic cells have 80S ribosomes whereas eukaryotic cells have 70S ribosomes.
    b. Both prokaryotic and eukaryotic cells have ribosomes.
    c. Chloroplasts and mitochondria have an envelope.
    d. Chloroplasts and mitochondria do not have organelles.

24. Which of the following events occurs during mitosis?
    a. DNA replication,
    b. replication of organelles,
    c. Splitting of the centromeres,
    d. Splitting of the cell.

25. During which phase of meiosis could crossing over occur?
    a. Prophase I,
    b. Prophase II,
    c. Metaphase I,
    d. Metaphase II.

26. Which one of the following molecules is involved in the control of the cell cycle?
    a. cyclins,
    b. cholesterol,
    c. carbohydrate,
    d. glycoprotein.

27. Several pieces of tissue from two different types of potato were bathed in salt solutions of differing concentrations and their percentage change in mass measured over a period of one hour.

Which one of the following statements is correct?
    a. There were more pieces of potato A then potato B.
    b. The pieces of potato B were smaller than the pieces of potato A.
    c. The cytoplasm of potato A cells had a lower solute concentration than potato B cells.
    d. The cytoplasm of potato B cells had a lower solute concentration than potato A cells.

28. A root tip was stained and observed under the light microscope. In the field of view there were 22 cells that were in one of the four phases of mitosis and 88 that were in interphase. The mitotic index was:
    a. 0.25,
    b. 0.2,
    c. 5.0,
    d. 4.0.

29. Karyotyping is a process whereby:
    a. genes are sorted according to size,
    b. genetic abnormalities can be marked on chromosomes,
    c. the number of chromosomes can be counted,
    d. chromosomes are sorted according to size and structure.

30. Which of the following shows a correct sequence of stages of the first division of meiosis?
    a. Prophase I, metaphase I, telophase I, anaphase I,
    b. Prophase I, anaphase I, metaphase I, telophase I,
    c. Prophase I, metaphase I, anaphase I, telophase I,
    d. Prophase I, telophase I, metaphase I, anaphase I.

31. Non-disjunction occurs as a result of:
    a. the two parts of meiosis occurring in reverse order,
    b. a failure in the spindle fibre network of microtubules,
    c. genes becoming lost,
    d. a failure in the process of cytokinesis.

32. Down syndrome is:
    a. an example of a trisomy,
    b. a result of non-disjunction in the sex chromosomes,
    c. due to a gene mutation,
    d. an example of karyotyping.

33. A haploid cell is one in which:
    a. only one of each pair of chromosomes is present,
    b. there are 23 chromosomes,
    c. the sex chromosomes are missing,
    d. there is no nucleus.

Chapter Four

Cell Metabolism

Metabolism is the web of all the enzyme catalysed reactions in a cell or organism.

Two major metabolic pathways are photosynthesis and respiration. Photosynthesis stores energy from sunlight in organic compounds such as glucose, and respiration then releases this energy which can be used for metabolic work such as active transport or protein synthesis.

Metabolic pathways are complex!

Designed by Donald Nicholson

©2002 International Union of Biochemistry and Molecular Biology

Metabolism

Key points

➤ Life is based carbon compounds.

➤ Four major groups of carbon compounds are:
- carbohydrates,
- lipids,
- proteins,
- nucleic acids.

➤ Metabolism is the web of all the enzyme catalysed reactions in a cell or organism.

➤ Anabolism is:
- the synthesis of complex organic molecules from simpler molecules,
- including formation of macromolecules from monomers by condensation reactions.

➤ Catabolism is:
- the breakdown of complex organic molecules into simpler molecules,
- including hydrolysis of macromolecules into monomers.

Enzymes

Key points

➤ Enzymes are key molecules in metabolism.

➤ They allow reactions to take place at physiological temperatures.

➤ Enzyme activity can be regulated so metabolic pathways can be controlled.

Lock and key model of enzyme action

Shape and chemistry of substrate –
corresponds to shape and chemistry of active site.

Key points

➤ Enzymes are large molecules folded to form a three-dimensional globular structure.

➤ The folding creates a specifically shaped three-dimensional 'pocket', the **active site**, on the surface.

➤ The substrate or substrates fit into the active site.

➤ The chemical properties of the active site match those of the substrates so they are chemically attached.

➤ Both enzyme and substrate(s) are moving around randomly in solution.

➤ Thus they will collide and the substrate(s) enter the active site.

➤ The substrates are brought together in the correct orientation for catalysis to occur.

➤ Enzymes can catalyse both catabolic and anabolic reactions.

Factors affecting enzyme action

Key background points

➢ Enzymes are proteins.
➢ They are large, complex folded molecules held in shape by, mostly, weak bonds.
➢ Increasing temperature makes atoms and molecules move more quickly.
➢ Hydrogen bonds and ionic bonds are affected by changes in pH – see page 39.

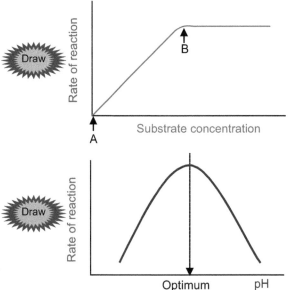

- We assume here that the amount of enzyme is fixed and therefore the number of active sites is constant.
- As substrate concentration increases between A and B more collisions occur with enzyme molecules and so more reactions occur.
- At point B all the active sites are occupied by substrate at any one time and so there can be no further increase in reaction rate.

- Enzymes are large protein molecules folded into a complex three-dimensional shape.
- This shape is held in place by bonds and these are strongest at the optimum pH.
- Changing the pH affects these bonds and so the shape of the molecule, and hence the active site, changes.
- If the substrate can no longer bind to the active site then the reaction rate drops.
- Note the symmetry of the curve.

- Note the asymmetry of this curve compared to the pH one.
- There is an approximately exponential increase up to the optimum temperature and then a sharp drop.
- Temperature increases the molecular movement and so in the solution the molecules collide more frequently and with more energy.
- This makes it more likely that the reaction occurs.
- However beyond the optimum temperature the amino acids within the protein are moving so much that weak bonds are broken and the molecule begins to fall apart.
- Once again the shape of the active site no longer fits the shape of the substrate and the reaction cannot take place.

Enzymes in biotechnology

➢ Enzymes are widely used in industry.
➢ It is often useful to immobilise the enzyme by fixing it to an inactive substance.
➢ An example is the production of lactose-free milk.

Production of lactose-free milk

Key points

➢ Many adults are intolerant of the lactose in milk.
➢ This is because as they get older the gene producing lactase gets switched off.
➢ Lactose is a disaccharide and cannot be absorbed by the gut.
➢ The lactose then gets fermented by bacteria in the large intestine resulting in nausea, abdominal pain and diarrhoea.
➢ Milk is treated with lactase and this breaks down the lactose to the monosaccharides glucose and galactose which are easily absorbed by the gut.
➢ Lactase is obtained from the fungus *K.lactis*.
➢ The lactase is often immobilised in alginate beads and the milk passed over it.

A simple laboratory set-up for producing lactose-free milk

Advantages of immobilised enzyme

Key points

➢ It can be used in a continuous flow system making it very efficient.

➢ The product is not mixed with the enzyme so no purification process is needed.

➢ It is more economical as the lactase can be used repeatedly.

➢ Since enzyme is not lost production time can be prolonged.

➢ The enzyme can be recovered to use again making the process more economical.

Uses of lactose-free milk

Key points

➢ The milk can be drunk by lactose-intolerant people as a source of calcium and vitamins.

➢ It is used in the production of ice cream as lactose crystallises when cold and makes the ice cream granular. The glucose and galactose remain dissolved and so the ice cream is smoother.

➢ In yoghurt production bacteria ferment lactose slowly but ferment glucose and galactose much more quickly making production faster.

➢ Lactose is not a sweet tasting sugar whereas glucose and galactose are. By changing the lactose into these two sugars foods such as yoghurt and ice cream made from lactose-free milk need less added sugar to make them taste sweet.

1. What is catabolism?	2. What is meant by the term 'denaturing'?	3. What is the name of the model of enzyme-substrate interaction?
4. State the region of an enzyme where the substrate binds.	5. What property must this region have for the substrate to bind?	
6a. Draw a graph to show the effect of substrate concentration on reaction rate.	6b. Explain the shape of the graph.	
7. Which enzyme curve is asymmetric – effect of temperature or effect of pH?	8. Why does increasing temperature denature an enzyme?	9. What is the opposite of catabolism?
10. What is the characteristic feature of molecules in solution which allows catalysis to take place?	11. What is an immobilised enzyme?	12. State one example of industrial use of an immobilised enzyme.
13. State two reasons why your example is of commercial value.	14. State two advantages of using an immobilised enzyme.	

Photosynthesis

Key points

➢ Photosynthesis is the production of carbon compounds in cells using light energy.
➢ Visible white light from the sun is composed of a range of wavelengths (colours).
➢ Red has the longest wavelength and violet the shortest.
➢ Chlorophyll absorbs red and blue light most effectively and reflects green light.
➢ Visible light has wavelengths between 400 and 700nm.

The **absorption spectrum** of chlorophyll shows how much of a particular wavelength is absorbed by the pigments.

An **action spectrum** shows how much photosynthesis takes place at a particular wavelength.

If the two are superimposed this clearly shows the close correlation, indicating that the light energy absorbed is used in the process of photosynthesis.

The difference between the two is because there are additional pigments in chloroplasts which absorb other wavelengths.

carotene

phaeophytin

xanthophyll

chlorophyll a

chlorophyll b

Diagram of chloroplast pigments separated by simple paper chromatography

Factors affecting the rate of photosynthesis

Rate of photosynthesis

Light intensity or
carbon dioxide concentration

1. **Light Intensity**
   As the intensity increases there comes a point when all the chlorophyll molecules are saturated and cannot accept any more light.
   A minimum intensity is required before photosynthesis starts.

2. **Carbon Dioxide**
   This is a substrate for an enzyme controlled reaction, and once all the enzyme active sites are used up the reaction cannot go faster. (Refer back to page 97).
   A minimum concentration of carbon dioxide is required before photosynthesis starts.

3. **Temperature**
   The shape of the graph should be familiar. (Refer back to page 97). Many of the reactions of photosynthesis are enzyme controlled and hence the rate of photosynthesis shows the same shape.

Rate of photosynthesis

Temperature

Limiting factors

Key point
➢ When a chemical process depends on more than one essential condition being favourable, its rate is limited by that factor which is nearest its minimum value.

Imagine a pizza production line. To make 10 pizzas requires:

10 bases	4 mushrooms
10 tomatoes	25 anchovies
150g grated cheese	20 olives

But suppose you only have 12 olives. This means that you can only make 6 pizzas, so the olives are the limiting factor.
Again suppose you have 12 olives but now only 5 tomatoes. Now you can only make 5 pizzas as this time it is the tomato that is the limiting factor.

D 0.13%CO_2 at 30^0C

C 0.13%CO_2 at 20^0C

B 0.03%CO_2 at 30^0C
A 0.03%CO_2 at 20^0C

Curves A and B are identical even though the temperature for B is 10^0C higher. This indicates that temperature is not the limiting factor.

If the carbon dioxide concentration is raised but the temperature kept at 20^0C the curve rises to C, indicating that the limiting factor for A and B was CO_2 concentration.

If the temperature is now raised to 30^0C the curve rises to D, indicating that the limiting factor for curve C was temperature.

The chloroplast

Key points

➢ Chloroplasts are the structures that carry out photosynthesis.

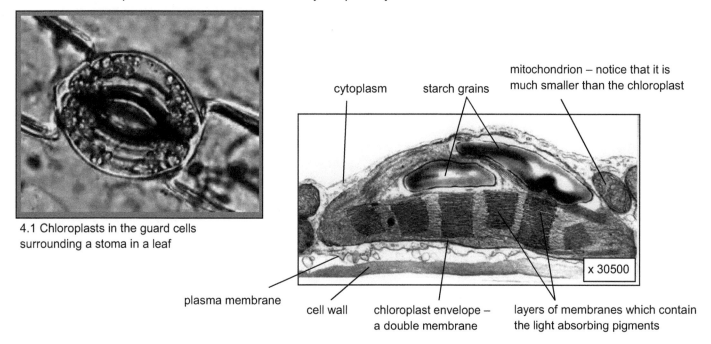

4.1 Chloroplasts in the guard cells surrounding a stoma in a leaf

cytoplasm   starch grains

mitochondrion – notice that it is much smaller than the chloroplast

x 30500

plasma membrane

cell wall   chloroplast envelope – a double membrane

layers of membranes which contain the light absorbing pigments

4.2 Electron micrograph of a chloroplast

Step 1

Photolysis

➢ Light energy is absorbed by the chlorophyll in the chloroplasts.
➢ The Light energy is used to:
  • split water into oxygen gas, hydrogen, and electrons
  • generate ATP
➢ The oxygen gas is excreted.

> Remember that lysis means to split; therefore photo – lysis means splitting with light.

Step 2

Carbon fixation

➢ The electron energy and ATP are used to combine carbon dioxide with hydrogen to make a triose sugar.
➢ The triose sugar is used to make other carbohydrates – glucose, sucrose, starch.
➢ The triose sugar is used to make other organic molecules – amino acids, fatty acids, glycerol, vitamins, nucleic acids.

Summary

Light energy

absorbed by chlorophyll

released as gas

Photolysis

Water ⟶ oxygen + hydrogen + electrons

electron energy and ATP

Carbon fixation

carbon dioxide + hydrogen ⟶ glucose and other organic molecules

Atmosphere, oceans, rocks and photosynthesis

Key points

➤ The early Earth's atmosphere was anaerobic so any organisms had to use inefficient anaerobic respiration.

➤ About 3.5 million years ago some prokaryotic organisms evolved the ability to harvest sunlight energy.

➤ The source of electrons was sulphur compounds which limited them to volcanic areas.

➤ About 2.5 million years ago another group of prokaryotes modified the light energy harvesting pathway which enabled them to extract electrons from water.

➤ These were the cyanobacteria.

➤ They were now able to exploit the vast areas covered by ocean.

➤ A by-product was oxygen released into the water and atmosphere.

➤ Initially all the oxygen was taken up by dissolved iron in the water and iron compounds in rocks to form iron oxides.

➤ Gradually oxygen began to remain dissolved in the oceans.

➤ This allowed the evolution of the much more efficient aerobic respiration pathway and marine organisms flourished.

➤ Huge quantities of carbon dioxide were removed from the atmosphere via the oceans into calcium carbonate in the shells and skeletons of marine organisms and these eventually formed massive chalk deposits.

➤ As more oxygen accumulated in the upper atmosphere it reacted with sunlight to form ozone.

➤ Ozone protects the Earth's surface from damaging ultraviolet light. (UV light causes DNA mutations).

➤ This allowed organisms to move onto the land.

4.3 The White Cliffs of Dover. These huge cliffs are chalk formed from tiny marine animals called Foraminifera.

15. Which colours in the spectrum are absorbed most during photosynthesis?	16. What is the range of wavelengths of light in the visible spectrum?	17. List two factors, other than carbon dioxide, that affect the rate of photosynthesis.

18. Distinguish between an absorption spectrum and an action spectrum.

19. Draw a graph to show the effect of carbon dioxide concentration on the rate of photosynthesis.

21. Draw graphs using the same axes to show the absorption spectrum of chlorophyll and an action spectrum.

20a. On your graph above draw an arrow to indicate where another factor becomes limiting.

20b. State which one of the factors you gave in Q17 is likely to be the limiting factor.

Respiration

Key points
- ➢ Cell respiration is the controlled release of energy from organic compounds to produce ATP.
- ➢ This ATP is immediately available as a source of energy in the cell.
- ➢ Two types:
  - anaerobic,
  - aerobic.
- ➢ Anaerobic respiration does not require oxygen.
- ➢ Aerobic respiration does require oxygen.
- ➢ The end product from anaerobic respiration, pyruvate, is used in aerobic respiration.

Step 1
Anaerobic
- ➢ The anaerobic pathway converts glucose to pyruvate.
- ➢ There is only a small yield of ATP per glucose molecule.
- ➢ It occurs in the cytoplasm.

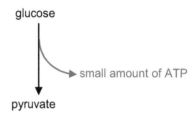

Step 2
Aerobic
- ➢ If oxygen is available the pyruvate enters the mitochondrion.
- ➢ It is oxidised using the oxygen breathed in.
- ➢ Carbon dioxide and water are released.
- ➢ A large amount of ATP is made.

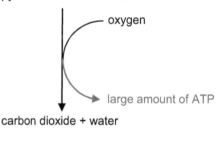

folded inner membrane of mitochondrial envelope contains the enzymes and other proteins for the aerobic pathway

4.4 TEM of a mitochondrion.

The anaerobic branches
- ➢ If oxygen is not available the pyruvate is switched to a branch anaerobic pathway.
- ➢ Muscle tissue and yeasts are both able to switch to this branch anaerobic pathway.

Muscle tissue
- ➢ This pathway is reversible.
- ➢ Muscle cells low in oxygen can switch to an anaerobic pathway in order to maintain a supply of ATP for contraction.
- ➢ The lactate is transferred to the liver where it can be converted back to pyruvate.
- ➢ This is very efficient.

Yeast:fermentation
- ➢ This pathway is not reversible.
- ➢ Large amounts of energy are wasted in the ethanol which is excreted.
- ➢ Use is made of the carbon dioxide to make bread rise and in producing sparkling wines and champagne.
- ➢ Ethanol is used in alcoholic drinks and as car fuel in some countries.

22a. In the first part of photosynthesis water is split. What is the name given to this reaction?	22b. List the three products of this reaction.	22c. Which of these products is excreted?
23a. What is the name of the second stage of photosynthesis?	23b. In this stage name the two molecules that are combined.	23c. What else is required in order to join these molecules?
24. Name the group of organisms that was able to extract electrons from water.	25. What happened to the oxygen that was at first released from splitting water?	26. What substance did marine organisms remove from the atmosphere in order to make their shells and skeletons?
27. In the anaerobic pathway in muscle what is pyruvate converted into?	28. In the anaerobic pathway in yeast what is pyruvate converted into?	29. Why is the muscle pathway more efficient than the yeast pathway?
30. Is the conversion of glucose to pyruvate aerobic or anaerobic?	31. In which part of the cell does the formation of pyruvate take place?	32. What is a lysis reaction?
33. What is the difference in ATP production between the first and second steps of respiration?	34. What are the end products from the second step in respiration?	35. Which molecule, other than pyruvate, is required for the second step?

Glossary

ABSORPTION SPECTRUM	The pattern of absorption of light (by chloroplast pigments) at different wavelengths.
ACTION SPECTRUM	The pattern of a chemical action (e.g. photosynthesis – production of oxygen) at different wavelengths of light.
AEROBIC	A chemical reaction that requires oxygen.
ANAEROBIC	A chemical reaction that can proceed without oxygen.
CONFORMATIONAL CHANGE	A change in the shape of a protein.
EXPONENTIAL INCREASE	An increase where the rate of increase continues to increase.
pH	The measure of the acidity or alkalinity of a solution. Neutral is a pH of 7, acids have a pH of less than 7 and alkalis a pH of more than 7.
PHYSIOLOGICAL TEMPERATURES	The temperature range within which most organisms live. Approximately $0 - 45^{0}$C.
SUBSTRATE	The organic molecule on which an enzyme acts.
SEM : TEM	Scanning electron micrograph : Transmission electron micrograph.

Answers to Grey Box Questions   **Underlined words are required.**

1.   The breaking down of complex organic molecules into simpler ones.
2.   The breakdown of the normal stable form of a protein.   3.   Lock and key.
4.   Active site.   5.   The same chemical properties as the substrate.

6a.

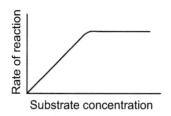

6b.   With more substrate the rate of reaction increases; eventually all the active sites are occupied at any one time an further addition of substrate has no effect.
7.   Effect of temperature.
8.   The molecules start moving faster and faster and eventually this movement breaks the weak bonds holding the shape of the molecule together.
9.   Anabolism.   10.   They are continually moving.
11.   An enzyme that has been attached to an inert/non-reactive base.
12.   Production of lactose-free milk.
13.   Some people are intolerant of lactose in milk; produces better quality ice-cream; yoghurt production is faster; glucose and galactose taste sweeter than lactose.
14.   The enzyme does not contaminate the product/does not need to be removed from the product; enzyme is not lost so costs cheaper; production can be on a continuous basis.
15.   Blue and red.   16.   400 – 700nm.
17.   Temperature; light intensity.
18.   Absorption spectrum – the range of wavelengths that are absorbed by the photosynthetic pigments; action spectrum – the amount of photosynthesis produced at different wavelengths.
19.

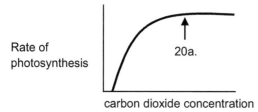

20b. Light intensity.
21.   See page 99.
22a. Photolysis.   22b. Electrons; protons; oxygen.   22c. Oxygen.
23a. Carbon fixation.   23b. Carbon dioxide; hydrogen.   23c. ATP and electron energy.
24.   Cyanobacteria.   25.   Taken up by/reacted with iron compounds to form iron oxides.
26.   Carbon dioxide.   27.   Lactate.   28.   Ethanol and carbon dioxide.
29.   The lactate can be converted back to pyruvate and recycled.
30.   Anaerobic.   31.   Cytoplasm.
32.   When a larger molecule is split into smaller ones.
33.   First step – small amount of ATP; second step – large amount of ATP.
34.   Carbon dioxide and water.   35.   Oxygen

Self-test Quiz

1. Anabolism can best be described as:
    a. the breakdown of macromolecules into their constituent monomers,
    b. the formation of peptide bonds during the synthesis of polypeptides,
    c. the formation of organic macromolecules from simpler molecules,
    d. building larger molecules using enzymes and ribosomes.

2. The active site of an enzyme is:
    a. the region of the molecule where the substrate can bind,
    b. the region of the molecule that is folded,
    c. the region of the molecule that is denatured by heating,
    d. the region of the molecule that is hydrophilic.

3. Which of the graphs represents the effect of temperature on the rate of an enzyme controlled reaction?

   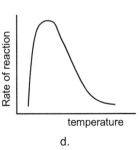

    a.   .b   c.   d.

4. An immobilised enzyme is one which:
    a. does not affect the rate of reaction,
    b. is not altered by the reaction,
    c. is attached to an inert substance,
    d. is fixed in the plasma membrane.

5. Which of the following graphs represents the absorption spectrum for photosynthesis?

  a.   amount of   b.   temperature   c.   wavelength   d.   wavelength
       absorption   of light   of light

6. Why is the action spectrum for photosynthesis similar to the absorption spectrum of chlorophyll?
    a. Because visible light has wavelengths between 400 and 700nm.
    b. Photosynthetic pigments such as chlorophyll function at the same optimum temperature as the enzymes used in photosynthesis.
    c. Only the energy in the wavelengths of light absorbed by photosynthetic pigments such as chlorophyll can be used in photosynthesis.
    d. All plants use the same photosynthetic pigments for photosynthesis.

7. Which of the following statements correctly describes a limiting factor?
    a. The optimum temperature at which an enzyme works.
    b. A variable factor that controls the rate of a process and is nearest to its minimum value.
    c. A variable factor in a sequence that functions at the slowest rate.
    d. A factor in a chemical chain that varies in concentration.

8. Which of the following graphs correctly shows that light intensity is acting as a limiting factor for photosynthesis?

a.

b.

c.

d.

9. If a beam of white light is shone through a solution of chlorophyll and the emerging beam split into colours by a prism, which colour or colours will be largely missing?
    a. red, blue and green,
    b. green,
    c. red and blue,
    d. red and green.

10. Light visible to the human eye has wavelengths between:
    a. 300 to 700nm.
    b. 400 to 800nm.
    c. 300 to 800nm.
    d. 400 to 700nm.

11. Which of the following statements about the photolysis reaction is correct?
    a. It splits water and oxygen is released.
    b. It requires light energy from the green part of the spectrum.
    c. It splits light into red and blue wavelengths.
    d. It splits glucose into carbon dioxide and water.

12. Which of the following statements about carbon fixation is correct?
    a. Carbon dioxide and oxygen from the atmosphere are combined to make glucose.
    b. ATP is used to combine carbon with hydrogen and oxygen to make organic compounds.
    c. Carbon dioxide and hydrogen are combined to make a triose sugar.
    d. ATP is used to convert triose sugars into glucose and other organic compounds.

13. The early Earth's atmosphere was anaerobic. Cyanobacteria evolved and released oxygen into the atmosphere. Which of the following was **not** a beneficial consequence of this?
    a. It resulted in the formation of the ozone layer.
    b. It allowed the evolution of the aerobic respiration pathway.
    c. Organisms could move onto land as the UV levels were reduced.
    d. It caused the atmosphere to warm up so organisms could move onto land.

14. Which of the following statements is correct?
    a. In muscle tissue glucose can be converted to lactate.
    b. In muscle tissue glucose can be converted to lactate and carbon dioxide.
    c. In yeast glucose can be converted to ethanol and water.
    d. In yeast glucose can be converted to lactate and carbon dioxide.

15. Which of the following statements about aerobic respiration is correct?
    a. Pyruvate is converted to carbon dioxide and water in the cytoplasm.
    b. Pyruvate is converted to carbon dioxide and water in mitochondria.
    c. Pyruvate is converted to carbon dioxide and ethanol in the mitochondria.
    d. Conversion of pyruvate to carbon dioxide and water in the mitochondria requires a large amount of ATP.

Chapter Five

Human Physiology

This chapter looks a few aspects of human anatomy and physiology. Although the chapter is set out as separate organ systems think of them as an overall integrated unit, the body.

The human gut

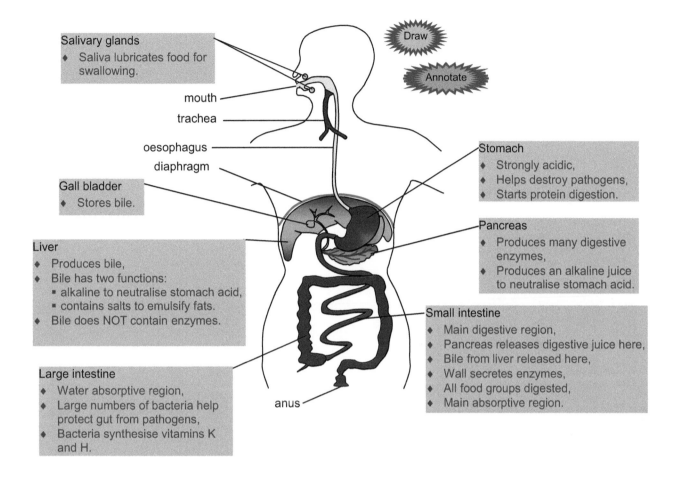

Salivary glands
- Saliva lubricates food for swallowing.

mouth

trachea

oesophagus

diaphragm

Gall bladder
- Stores bile.

Liver
- Produces bile,
- Bile has two functions:
  - alkaline to neutralise stomach acid,
  - contains salts to emulsify fats.
- Bile does NOT contain enzymes.

Large intestine
- Water absorptive region,
- Large numbers of bacteria help protect gut from pathogens,
- Bacteria synthesise vitamins K and H.

anus

Draw

Annotate

Stomach
- Strongly acidic,
- Helps destroy pathogens,
- Starts protein digestion.

Pancreas
- Produces many digestive enzymes,
- Produces an alkaline juice to neutralise stomach acid.

Small intestine
- Main digestive region,
- Pancreas releases digestive juice here,
- Bile from liver released here,
- Wall secretes enzymes,
- All food groups digested,
- Main absorptive region.

Digestion
Key facts
- Large molecules cannot pass through the wall of the villus.
- Large molecules need to be broken down into their constituent units in order to be reassembled in the way the body wants.
- Macromolecules – starch, glycogen, lipids and nucleic acids – are digested into monomers.
- Cellulose is undigested.
- Without enzymes the reactions are too slow at body temperature.

Pancreatic enzymes
Key facts
- The pancreatic duct carries pancreatic juices to the duodenum.
- Pancreatic juice contains:
  - alkaline salts to help neutralise the acidic stomach juices,
  - many enzymes.

Enzyme	Substrate
Amylase	Starch
Endopeptidase	Proteins
Lipase	Lipid

Digestion of starch
- Amylase breaks starch down to maltose.
- Maltase breaks maltose into glucose.
- The glucose is actively transported into the villus cells.
- Maltase is attached to the outer plasma membrane of the villus cells.

The gut wall

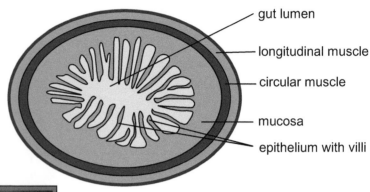

The small intestine is divided into two regions.
1. Duodenum leads from the stomach and is where the bile and pancreatic ducts join.
2. Ileum, which is much longer, and is the main absorptive region.

gut lumen

longitudinal muscle

circular muscle

mucosa

epithelium with villi

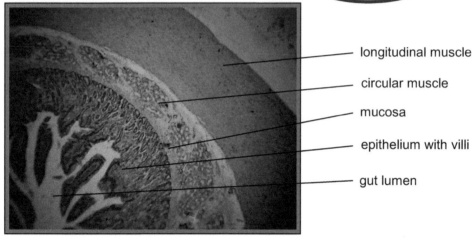

longitudinal muscle

circular muscle

mucosa

epithelium with villi

gut lumen

5.1 Cross section of the small intestine

Dialysis tubing

➢ This is an artificially permeable membrane.
➢ It can be used for digestion investigations.
  ▪ Example:

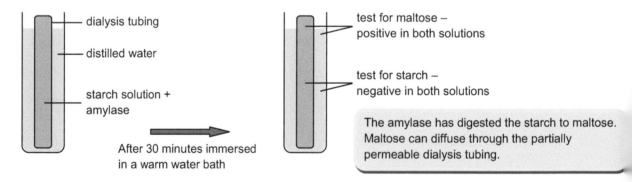

dialysis tubing

distilled water

starch solution + amylase

After 30 minutes immersed in a warm water bath

test for maltose – positive in both solutions

test for starch – negative in both solutions

The amylase has digested the starch to maltose. Maltose can diffuse through the partially permeable dialysis tubing.

Peristalsis

➢ This is the contraction of the circular and longitudinal muscles in a wave motion.
➢ This:
  • mixes the food with the enzymes,
  • moves the food along the gut.

circular muscles contracted

circular muscles relaxed

food

circular muscles contract in a wave which pushes the food along the gut.

Absorption

This is done through the millions of villi lining the wall of the small intestine.

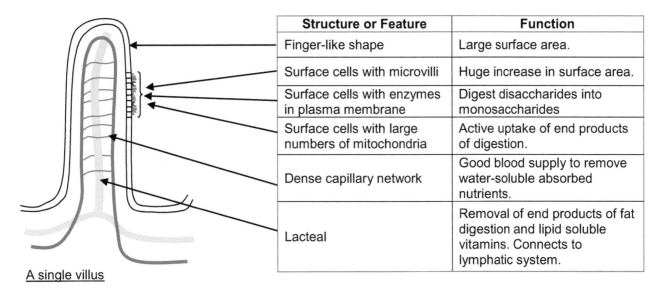

Structure or Feature	Function
Finger-like shape	Large surface area.
Surface cells with microvilli	Huge increase in surface area.
Surface cells with enzymes in plasma membrane	Digest disaccharides into monosaccharides
Surface cells with large numbers of mitochondria	Active uptake of end products of digestion.
Dense capillary network	Good blood supply to remove water-soluble absorbed nutrients.
Lacteal	Removal of end products of fat digestion and lipid soluble vitamins. Connects to lymphatic system.

A single villus

Key points

➢ Villi are tiny folds in the gut wall epithelium.
➢ Villus surface cells have microvilli.
➢ Together they bring about a huge increase in surface area.
➢ The monomer end products of digestion are absorbed over the villus surface.
➢ Mineral ions are absorbed over the villus surface.
➢ Methods of absorption over the villus surface are:
  - simple diffusion,
  - facilitated diffusion, ⎫ see pages 69–71.
  - active transport, ⎬
  - pinocytosis. ⎭
➢ Absorbed substances are transferred to the blood stream and lacteal for transport to the liver.

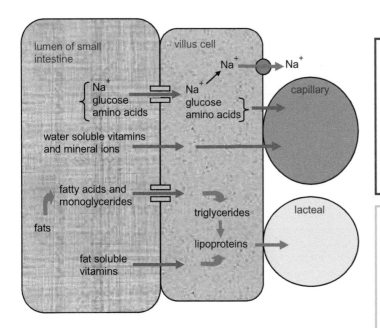

Capillary
- Sodium ions are actively transported out of the villus cell.
- This creates a diffusion gradient.
- Sodium ions combine with glucose or amino acid molecules to diffuse through a facilitated diffusion co-transporter channel.
- Glucose and amino acids diffuse into the capillary through facilitated diffusion channels.

Lacteal
- Fatty acids and monoglycerides diffuse through facilitated diffusion channels into the villus cell.
- They are recombined into triglycerides.
- These are combined with phospholipids, cholesterol and proteins to make lipoproteins.
- Fat soluble vitamins combine with the lipoproteins.
- These leave the villus cell by exocytosis and most enter the lacteal.
- Some lipoprotein enters the capillary.

villi

mucosa

muscle

5.2a Low power view of villi

capillaries and lacteal

villus cells absorb end products of digestion

goblet cells produce mucus

microvilli

5.2b Tip of a villus

1. State the function of the gall bladder.	2. State two features about the stomach.	3. Is the pH of pancreatic juice alkaline or acidic?
4. State two functions of the small intestine.	5. State two functions of the large intestine.	6. State two functions of bile.
7. List two pancreatic enzymes other than endopeptidase.	8. State the function of endopeptidase.	9. Name the enzyme that breaks starch into maltose.
10. Name the enzyme that breaks maltose into glucose.	11. State precisely where the enzyme named in Q10 is found.	12. State the transport mechanism to transfer glucose into villus cells.
13. Where is the glucose transported to after it enters the blood stream?	14. Give two reasons why digestion is necessary.	15. Why are digestive enzymes necessary?
16. Name the two regions of the small intestine.		17. Name the process which moves food along the gut.
18. Name the two muscles that bring about the movement state in Q17.	19. List 5 features of a villus related to its role in absorption.	20. Name the region of the gut into which pancreatic juices are released.
		21. Name a dietary component that is not digested.

Gas exchange

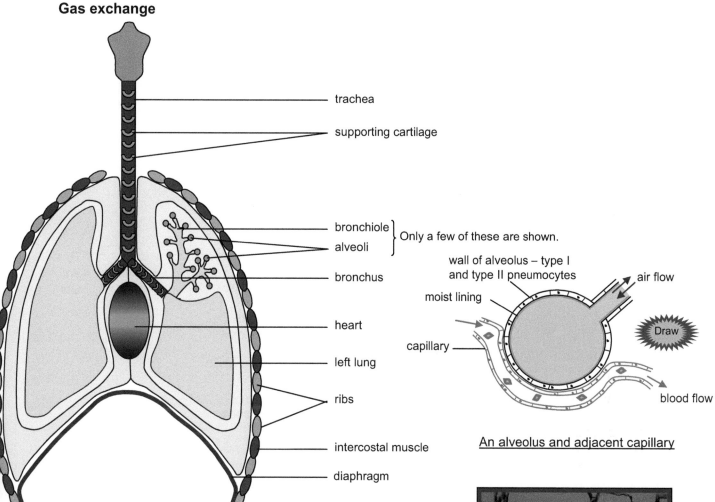

- trachea
- supporting cartilage
- bronchiole ⎱
- alveoli ⎰ Only a few of these are shown.
- bronchus
- heart
- left lung
- ribs
- intercostal muscle
- diaphragm

wall of alveolus – type I and type II pneumocytes
moist lining
capillary
air flow
Draw
blood flow

<u>An alveolus and adjacent capillary</u>

Alveoli

Key points

➢ Very small so large surface area to volume ratio.
➢ Wall of single layer of flattened cells called pneumocytes.
➢ Type I pneumocytes are the most common type.
➢ They are extremely thin to allow efficient gas exchange.
➢ Type II pneumocytes secrete a solution containing a surfactant.
➢ This surfactant creates:
  - a moist surface to assist gas exchange,
  - prevents the walls of the alveoli adhering to each other.
➢ Covered in dense capillary network.

Ventilation

Key points

➢ As oxygen diffuses into blood, carbon dioxide diffuses out of blood, concentration gradients decrease.
➢ Ventilation brings in fresh oxygen and removes carbon dioxide, which maintains concentration gradients.
➢ Steep diffusion gradients of oxygen and carbon dioxide between alveolar air and alveolar blood capillaries results in rapid diffusion of gases.

Tip: Type I pneumocytes are thin and I is thinner than II.

Note the very thin walls containing both the alveolus wall and the capillaries.   alveoli

5.3a Healthy lung tissue.

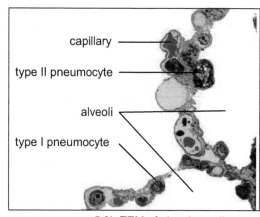

- capillary
- type II pneumocyte
- alveoli
- type I pneumocyte

5.3b TEM of alveolar walls.

Mechanism of ventilation

Principles

- ➤ The thoracic cavity is a sealed box.
- ➤ Atmospheric pressure is effectively constant.
- ➤ If the volume of the thoracic cavity increases the pressure decreases.
- ➤ Atmospheric pressure forces air into the lungs.
- ➤ If the volume of the thoracic cavity decreases the pressure increases.
- ➤ Air is forced out of the lungs.
- ➤ Two sets of antagonistic muscles work to carry out ventilation.

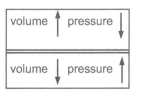

External intercostal muscles	Attached to the rib cage. When contract rib cage moves up **and** out. Volume increases; pressure decreases → breathe in. Internal intercostal muscles relaxed.
Internal intercostal muscles	Attached to the rib cage. When contract rib cage moves down **and** in. Volume decreases; pressure increases → breathe out. External intercostal muscles relaxed.
Diaphragm	Dome shaped structure separating thoracic cavity from abdominal cavity. When radial muscle contracts dome flattens. Volume increases; pressure decreases → breathe in.
Abdominal muscles	Abdominal muscles contract and push diaphragm back to dome shape. Volume decreases; pressure increases → breathe out. Diaphragm muscle relaxed.

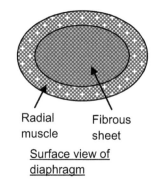

Surface view of diaphragm

Measuring ventilation

- ➤ Instruments such as a spirometer can measure various lung volumes.
- ➤ Breathing normally in and out produces the **tidal volume**.

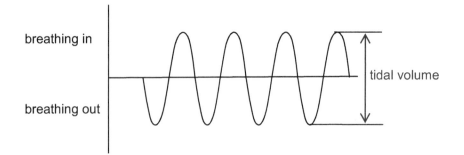

Ventilation rate is the number of breaths per minute.

The graph shows 4 breaths.

Lung cancer

Causes

- • The vast majority of cases are caused by smoking, especially cigarettes.
- • The rest are due to carcinogenic particles such as coal or asbestos dust breathed in.

Consequences

- • If detected early enough the tumour, or entire lung can be removed.
- • Death.

tumours

normal lung tissue that is being compressed

5.4a X-ray of lung tumours   5.4b Stained section of lung tumour

Emphysema

Key point

➢ Alveolar walls are broken down resulting in the reduction of surface area for gas exchange.

Causes

- The vast majority of cases are caused by smoking.

Consequences

- Difficulty in breathing.
- Gradual loss of ability to carry out any exercise and eventually even slow walking becomes nearly impossible.
- Breathing oxygen through a face mask or nasal tubes may be necessary in order to get enough oxygen into the blood.

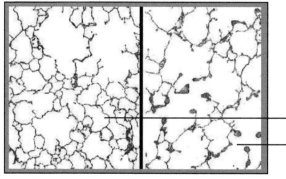

normal healthy lung

lung with emphysema

5.5 Healthy and damaged lung tissue.

1. Name the two cell types in the alveolus wall.	2. State the function of each cell type.	3. What is the purpose of ventilation?
4. What happens to thoracic pressure when the volume increases?	5. List two muscles which cause the thoracic volume to increase.	6. List two muscles which cause the thoracic volume to decrease.
7. Muscle work in pairs. What is the name given to this pair?	8. What is the name given to the volume of air breathed in and out in a normal breath?	9. What is ventilation rate?

10. Draw an alveolus and attached capillary.

11. State the major cause of lung cancer.

12. What is cancer?

13. State a possible consequence of lung cancer.

14. What is emphysema?

15. State a major cause of emphysema.

16. State a possible consequence of emphysema.

The blood system

The circulatory system
Key facts

➢ The heart is a double pump.
➢ The right side is the pulmonary circuit.
➢ The left side is the systemic circuit.
➢ Arteries carry blood away from the heart at high pressure.
  (**A**rteries – **A**way)
➢ Veins carry blood to the heart at low pressure.
➢ Pressure in the pulmonary artery is lower than pressure in the aorta.
➢ Valves in the veins and heart ensure a one-way flow in the circulatory system.
➢ The blood leaving the gut goes directly to the liver via the hepatic portal vein.

Blood is composed of:
♦ Plasma,
♦ Erythrocytes (red cells),
♦ Leucocytes (white cells):
  ▪ Phagocytes,
  ▪ Lymphocytes.
♦ Platelets.

Transported by the blood:
♦ Nutrients,
♦ Oxygen,
♦ Carbon dioxide,
♦ Hormones,
♦ Antibodies,
♦ Urea,
♦ Heat.

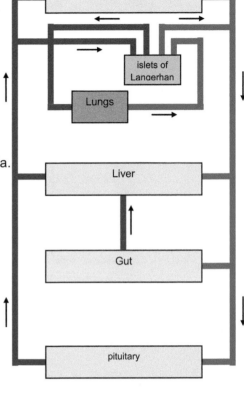

Heart

The mammalian double circulation

Transport by the blood

Key points

➢ Blood is mostly water which is a polar solvent – see pages 18–19.
➢ Polar molecules such as glucose, amino acids and sodium chloride dissolve.
➢ Oxygen also dissolves.
➢ Fats are non-polar and do not dissolve.
➢ Cholesterol is only very slightly soluble.
➢ Fats and cholesterol are transported as lipoproteins – see page 23.

The heart

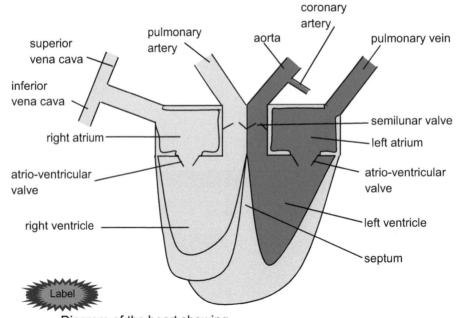

Diagram of the heart showing
chambers, blood vessels and valves

IBSL Biology 2016 © Ashby Merson-Davies

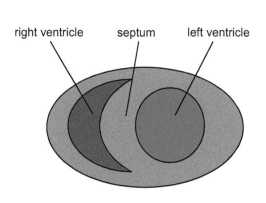

right ventricle   septum   left ventricle

Horizontal section through the ventricles

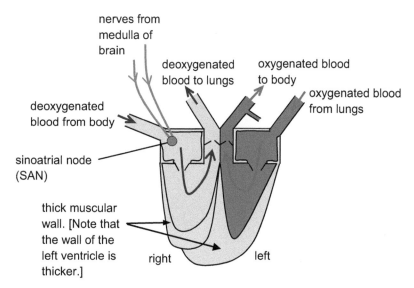

nerves from medulla of brain

deoxygenated blood to lungs

oxygenated blood to body

oxygenated blood from lungs

deoxygenated blood from body

sinoatrial node (SAN)

thick muscular wall. [Note that the wall of the left ventricle is thicker.]

right

left

Diagram of the heart showing nerve supply and blood flow

arteries to arms and head

anterior vena cava

aorta

pulmonary artery

pulmonary vein

left atrium

right atrium

left ventricle

posterior vena cava

5.6 External view of the heart.

Control of the heartbeat

Key points
> The sinoatrial node, SAN, is a small patch of special muscle tissue on the wall of the right atrium near the point where the vena cava enters.
> The SAN acts as a pacemaker.
> It releases an electrical impulse approximately 70 times per minute.
> The electrical impulse is propagated (transmitted) through the heart muscle.
> This causes the atrial heart muscle to contract, followed by the ventricular muscle.
> Involuntary nerves from the cardiac control centre in the medulla of the brain are attached to the pacemaker.
> Impulses down the cardiac depressor nerve cause the heart rate to slow down, e.g. during sleep.
> Impulses down the cardiac accelerator nerve cause the heart rate to speed up, e.g. during exercise.
> The hormone epinephrine (adrenalin) from the adrenal gland stimulates the pacemaker causing the heart rate to speed up in preparation for vigorous physical activity.

Pressure changes in the left side of the heart and the aorta

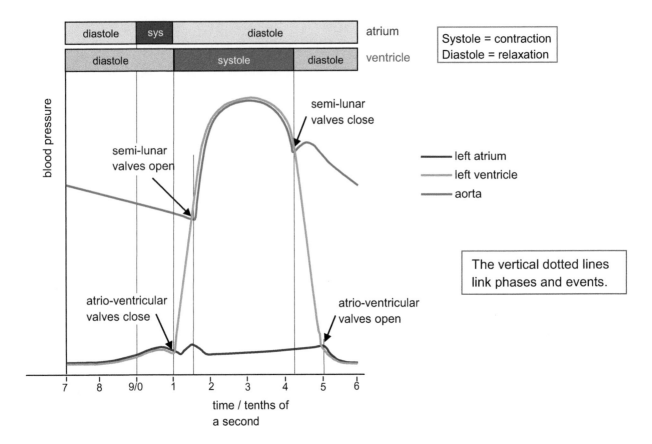

Systole = contraction
Diastole = relaxation

— left atrium
— left ventricle
— aorta

The vertical dotted lines link phases and events.

time / tenths of a second

The cardiac cycle

Key stages
Relate these events to the graphs above. Times are in tenths of a second.

Time 0 – 1
Atrial systole
➤ SAN (see page 115) fires when the ventricles are about 70% full.
➤ Atria contract filling ventricles further. Note the volume rises sharply.

Time 1 – 4.2
Ventricular systole
➤ Ventricles contract.
➤ Increase in pressure immediately closes atrio-ventricular valves.
➤ The flaps of the valves striking together as they close create the first of the two heart sounds.
➤ The pressure increases further until the semi-lunar valve is opened allowing blood to flow into the aorta.
➤ At this time the volume decreases.

Time 4.2 – 9
Ventricular diastole
➤ Ventricles relax.
➤ Back pressure of blood in arteries causes semi-lunar valves to snap shut.
➤ The flaps striking together cause the second of the two heart sounds.
➤ Blood pressure in the vena cava pushes blood into the atria.
➤ Elastic recoil of the ventricular muscle lowers ventricular pressure.
➤ As soon as ventricular pressure is below the atrial pressure the atrio-ventricular valves open and the ventricle start to fill rapidly at first but then more slowly.

IBSL Biology 2016 © Ashby Merson-Davies

Occlusion (blockage) of the coronary arteries

Causes

➢ A high LDL:HDL ratio in the blood stream – see page 23.
➢ Results in a fatty deposit, a plaque or atheroma, forming in the walls of the coronary arteries.
➢ This is called atherosclerosis.
➢ This restricts blood flow.
➢ This results in coronary heart disease or CHD.
➢ The plaque can stimulate the formation of a blood clot.
➢ The clot could break free and lodge in a smaller artery.

Consequences

➢ Reduction in oxygenated blood flow to the heart muscle reduces respiration.
➢ Reduction in respiration lowers availability of ATP.
➢ Reduced ATP means the ventricular muscles work less efficiently.
➢ This causes pain in the heart called angina.
➢ If the blood flow is completely blocked this can produce a heart attack.

5.7 An atheroma in a carotid artery

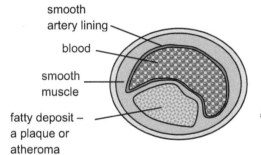

smooth artery lining
blood
smooth muscle
fatty deposit – a plaque or atheroma

An occlusion in an artery

The blood vessels

	Structure	Function
Arteries	Thick muscular wall	Withstand high pressure. Contracts to increase blood pressure.
	Elastic fibres	Stretched by pulse and when contract help to maintain steady blood flow.
	Collagen fibres	Tough inelastic fibres protect and prevent the wall from being over stretched.
	Endothelium	Smooth lining.
Capillaries	Wall of single layer of flattened cells	Reduced distance for diffusion between blood and tissues.
	Narrow lumen	Increased surface area.
	No muscle, elastic or fibrous tissue	Facilitate diffusion as substances only have to pass through a single layer of cells. Some capillaries have small gaps between the cells.
Veins	Endothelium	Smooth lining.
	Large lumen	Reduces resistance to flow.
	Some collagen, muscle and elastic fibres	Mainly protection.
	Valves	Prevent backflow when pressure very low.
	Thin walls	Allows vein to be squashed between muscle blocks which pumps the blood.

Transverse section of artery

basement membrane

flow

Longitudinal section of vein

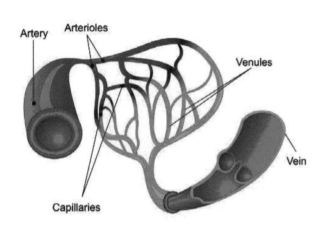

5.9a The relationship between artery, capillaries and vein

5.9b The relationship between capillaries and veins

artery

vein

5.8 Cross sections of an artery and a vein. Note the distinct difference in wall thickness

capillaries ⟶ venules ⟶ vein

IBSL Biology 2016 © Ashby Merson-Davies

5.10a Wall of an artery	5.10b Wall of a vein

Labels: lumen, endothelium, muscle and elastic fibres, collagen and elastic fibres

William Harvey's discovery of circulation
Born Folkestone, UK 1578

➤ Earlier views on blood were that when it was pumped out from the heart it was 'used up' in the body or turned to 'vapour' in the lungs and fresh blood 'made' in the liver.

➤ Harvey disproved this by measuring the volume of the heart and multiplying this by the number of heart beats in a day.

Volume of left and right ventricles = $140cm^3$

Number of beats per 24 hours = 75 beats per minute × 60 × 24 = 108,000 beats

Volume of blood pumped per 24 hours = 108000 × 140 = 15,120 litres

➤ Harvey stated that it would be impossible for the liver to generate this volume of blood.

➤ Therefore the blood must circulate around the body, pumped out from the heart and then returning to it.

➤ He was aware of arteries and veins and that these vessels repeatedly branched, but had to propose that there must be tiny connecting vessels that could not be seen. (The microscope had been invented in Harvey's time but it was not widely known about and Harvey did not have one).

➤ He showed that blood in veins can only flow one way due to valves.

5.11a

blood in veins

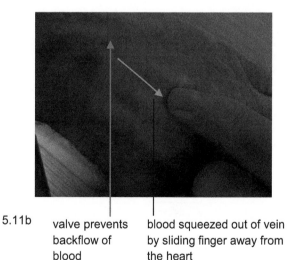

5.11b

valve prevents backflow of blood

blood squeezed out of vein by sliding finger away from the heart

5.11 A valve in action

1. What is meant by the term double circulation?	2. Which side of the heart is the pulmonary circuit?	3. What is the name of the other circuit?
4. Name the blood vessel supplying blood to the heart muscle.	5. Where does blood from the gut go to?	6. Is blood pressure highest in arteries or veins?
7. Name the blood vessel attached to the right atrium.	8. Name the blood vessel attached to the left ventricle.	9. Name the valve between the atrium and ventricle.
10. Name the valve in the base of the pulmonary artery.	11. Which wall of the heart is thickest?	12. To which chamber of the heart is the pulmonary vein attached?
13a. Name the structure in the heart which acts as a pacemaker.	13b. Where in the heart is this structure found?	13c. What is the function of this structure?
13d. Two nerves are attached to this structure. Where do they come from?	13e. What is the function of these two nerves?	14. Name the hormone that affects heart rate.
15. Which gland produces this hormone?	16. What is the function of the valves in the heart?	17. Is contraction of the heart systole or diastole?
18a. What causes the left atrio-ventricular valve to close?	18b. What causes the aortic semilunar valves to open?	18c. What causes the aortic semilunar valves to close?
19. What can cause an occlusion of the coronary artery?	20. What is the consequence of a coronary occlusion?	21. Which type of blood vessel has valves?
22. What is the function of the elastic fibres in the arteries?	23. Name the molecule in arterial walls which prevents overstretching.	24. What is the function of the muscle in arterial walls?

25. List two features of capillary walls which promote transport through them.

Defence against infectious disease

Key points
- ➢ A pathogen is an organism or virus that can cause infectious disease.
- ➢ Most pathogens are species specific.
- ➢ Some pathogens can cross the species barrier.
- ➢ Specificity is due to the ability to recognise unique molecules on the surface of its host cells.

> Viruses are not organisms because they are not living.

Pathogenic organisms
Include bacteria, fungi, protozoans, flatworms and tapeworms.
They can infect the skin, gut, liver, blood stream, brain and nervous system.

5.12 Tapeworm in the small intestine.

5.13 *Entomophthora muscae*
A fungal infection of a fly.

> Both HIV and the Ebola virus appear to have crossed the species barrier from wild animals to humans.

Antibiotics

Key points
- ➢ Act against specific chemicals or chemical pathways in prokaryotes.
- ➢ Hence do not affect eukaryotic cells.
- ➢ Some strains of bacteria have evolved genes that confer resistance to specific antibiotics.
- ➢ Some strains of bacteria have evolved multiple antibiotic resistance – see page 193.
- ➢ Viruses are intra-cellular parasites and lack metabolism.
- ➢ They use the host cell chemical pathways.
- ➢ Hence any drugs used against viruses would damage the host cell.

Florey and Chain
- ➢ Alexander Fleming accidentally discovered the penicillin fungus in 1928 but he was not aware of what use could be made of it.
- ➢ Ten years later Florey and Chain, along with a team of biochemists, produced enough penicillin to test in mice.
- ➢ They first injected healthy mice with penicillin to test its toxicity and found it had no effect.
- ➢ A group of mice were injected with haemolytic streptococci bacteria.
- ➢ Half of the group was then injected with penicillin.
- ➢ Several hours later the mice that received the penicillin were alive but those that had not were all dead.
- ➢ On the basis of this single success a toxicity test case in humans was proposed.
- ➢ A patient with terminal cancer agreed to the toxicity test but started shaking and developed a high fever.
- ➢ It was shown that these symptoms were due to impurities in the sample.
- ➢ The first human patient (trialled in 1941) was suffering from a bacterial infection of a wound.
- ➢ He was injected with a purified penicillin preparation and showed immediate signs of recovery.
- ➢ Insufficient penicillin was available to continue treatment and the patient later died.
- ➢ Further trials proved its effectiveness and production on a large scale was started in America.

Primary defence
1. Surface barriers

Key points – skin
- Dead waterproof surface layer.
- Tough, elastic.
- Oily secretion (sebum) from sebaceous gland in hair follicle controls fungal and bacterial growth and stops skin cracking. Sebum contains fatty acids.
- Dry – discourages growth of pathogens.
- Surface layer continually shed which removes pathogens.
- Cuts in the skin can be sealed by blood clotting.

Key points – mucous membranes
- In air passages sticky mucus traps pathogens, swept up to throat by ciliated cells and swallowed.
- In vagina, acidic (due to bacterial activity) to prevent growth of pathogens.
- Enzyme lysozyme in mucus kills bacteria.

2. Blood clotting cascade

5.14 A blood clot showing red cells and platelets (white) trapped in a mesh of fibrin fibres

Fibrin is an insoluble fibrous protein. The fibres become entangled and create a mesh in which red blood cells become trapped, blocking blood flow.

Secondary defence
1. Non-specific

Phagocytes
- These white blood cells ingest pathogens such as bacteria and viruses by endocytosis.
- They contain many lysosomes which contain digestive enzymes – see page 60.
- These enzymes destroy the pathogens.
- They can leave capillaries and enter tissues.
- They are able to identify pathogens by detecting foreign proteins on the pathogen surface.
- They are assisted by antibodies attached to pathogens.
- They concentrate at sites of infection.

2. Specific – antibody production

Antigens and antibodies
- An antigen is a molecule, usually a protein, which is foreign to the body and stimulates the production of a specific antibody.
- Every organism has unique molecules on the surface of its cells.
- These molecules can act as antigens.
- An antibody is a specific protein produced by the body in response to a specific antigen.
- The antibody producing cells are called lymphocytes.
- Lymphocytes can only produce one specific type of antibody.
- There are a large number of different types of lymphocyte in the body.

Large numbers of
lymphocyte types,
each with different
antibody

Pathogen with
antigen

antibody selects
antigen

lymphocyte activated and
divides to form a clone

activated lymphocytes
secrete large amounts
of antibody

pathogen
destroyed

HIV and the immune system

Key points

➢ HIV – Human Immunodeficiency Virus.
➢ The virus destroys a type of lymphocyte (called a Helper T lymphocyte) that is required to activate the antibody producing lymphocytes.
➢ This stage is shown by the green arrow on the diagram above.
➢ These lymphocytes therefore cannot be activated to form antibody secreting cells.
➢ Antibodies are not produced and the pathogen survives to cause an infection.
➢ This leads to the development of AIDS – Acquired Immuno-Deficiency Syndrome.
➢ Infections begin to accumulate in the body – the lungs are especially vulnerable.

Transmission of HIV

♦ Unprotected sexual intercourse, vaginal or anal.
♦ Oral sex.
♦ During birth.
♦ Breast feeding.
♦ Blood transfusion.
♦ Contaminated needles.
♦ Across placenta but this is rare.

1. What is a pathogen?

2. Why do antibiotics not work against viruses?

3. What did Florey and Chain discover using mice?

4. What are the two surface barriers that provide primary defence?

5a. In the blood clotting cascade what starts the process?

5b. Name the blood component that releases clotting factors.

5c. Name the molecule that causes fibrinogen fibres to form fibrin.

6. Name the blood component that forms the non-specific secondary defence.

7. Distinguish between an antibody and an antigen.

8a. Which type of blood cell is destroyed by HIV?

8b. How does this result in reduced immunity?

9. List three ways HIV can be transmitted.

The nervous system

The nervous system
The nervous system is one of two systems that control the body, the endocrine system being the other one – see page 129.
It consists of:

➤ a central nervous system (CNS)
  • brain and spinal cord,
➤ a peripheral nervous system (PNS).
  • two types of nerve cell or neuron:
    sensory neurons and motor neurons.

Sensory and motor neurons connect with other neurons in the CNS and these connections are called synapses.

5.15

Neurons

Key points

➤ Sensory neurons carry electrical impulses from receptors towards the central nervous system.
➤ Motor neurons carry electrical impulses away from the central nervous system to effectors.
➤ Neurons are covered by special cells which act as insulation.
➤ This insulating layer is called a myelin sheath.
➤ There are small gaps between these cells called nodes of Ranvier.

A motor neuron with myelin sheath

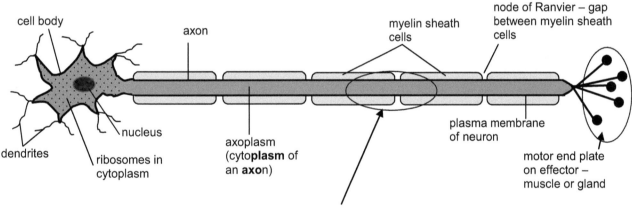

cell body
axon
myelin sheath cells
node of Ranvier – gap between myelin sheath cells
nucleus
axoplasm (cyto**plasm** of an **axo**n)
plasma membrane of neuron
dendrites
ribosomes in cytoplasm
motor end plate on effector – muscle or gland

This is the region enlarged in the following sequence of diagrams but without myelin sheath cells.

Neuron potentials

Key vocabulary

• Sodium-potassium ion linked pump.
• Open facilitated potassium ion channel.
• Voltage gated sodium ion channel.
• Voltage gated potassium ion channel.
• Axoplasm.
• Threshold value.
• Potential difference.
• Resting potential.
• Action potential.
• Depolarisation.
• Repolarisation.

Potential difference
This is the electrical difference between the positive and negative regions. It is the same as a battery – a 1.5 volt AA battery has a potential difference of 1.5 volts between the positive and negative ends.

Voltage gated channels
These facilitated channels have gates which control the flow of ions through them. The gate is normally in the closed position, but a change in voltage causes a conformational change which opens the gate.

1. Resting potential

Key facts

- ➤ This is the potential difference when the neuron is not transmitting an impulse.
- ➤ Sodium ions are actively pumped out of the neuron.
- ➤ Potassium ions are actively pumped into the neuron.
- ➤ Potassium ions diffuse out of the axoplasm through an open facilitated diffusion channel.
- ➤ Negative ions remain in the axoplasm.
- ➤ This generates the resting potential.

For every 3 Na^+ pumped out 2 K^+ are pumped in and one molecule of ATP is used.

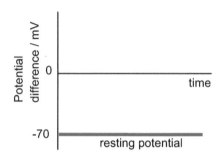

Note on the diagram that the minimum number of ions is shown to indicate concentration gradients. A red arrow indicates active transport and a green arrow diffusion.

2. Action potential

Key points

- ➤ The action potential has two parts:
  - • Depolarisation,
  - • Repolarisation.
- ➤ Nerve impulses are action potentials propagated (passed) along the axons of neurons.

Depolarisation

Key points

- ➤ A stimulus causes the sodium gated facilitated diffusion channel to open briefly.
- ➤ This allows a few sodium ions to diffuse into the axoplasm.
- ➤ The axoplasm starts to become less negative.
- ➤ If insufficient sodium ions diffuse in it fails to reach the threshold potential and it returns to the resting potential. ▬▬▬
- ➤ If it reaches the threshold potential it continues and changes from a negative potential to a positive potential. ▬▬▬
- ➤ This is depolarisation.

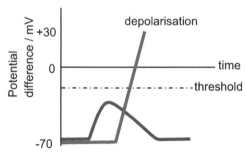

Repolarisation

➢ The potassium gated facilitated diffusion channel opens briefly.
➢ More potassium ions can now diffuse out of the axoplasm making the axoplasm less positive.
➢ The sodium ions that diffused in are now pumped out.
➢ The axoplasm returns to the resting potential.

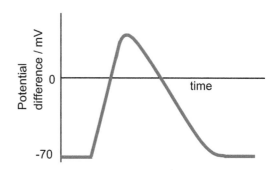

Transmission of an impulse

➢ When depolarisation occurs at a node of Ranvier local currents stimulate the next node to become depolarised.
➢ This is done by causing the voltage gated sodium channel to open.
➢ Thus the impulse jumps from node to node.
➢ This is called **saltatory conduction**.

5.16a Section through a
nerve – low magnification

5.16b Section through a
nerve – high magnification

Synapses
- ➤ A synapse is a junction where a neuron connects with another neuron.
- ➤ The signal is carried across the gap by a chemical called a neurotransmitter.
- ➤ An example of a neurotransmitter is acetyl choline.

Sequence of events
1. An incoming impulse opens a gated sodium channel causing depolarisation of the presynaptic membrane.
2. This opens a gated calcium channel allowing calcium ions to diffuse into the presynaptic bulb.
3. The calcium ions cause vesicles of neurotransmitter to attach to the presynaptic membrane.
4. The neurotransmitter is released by exocytosis, diffuses across the gap and binds to specific receptors on the postsynaptic membrane.
5. This causes a gated sodium channel to open which causes depolarisation of the postsynaptic bulb.
6. This opens a gated sodium channel which initiates the postsynaptic impulse.
7. The acetyl choline is hydrolysed by an enzyme (acetyl cholinesterase) into acetate and choline, transported into the presynaptic bulb and re-synthesised into new vesicles.

Blocking synaptic transmission
Key facts
- ➤ Some natural and synthetic chemicals can mimic neurotransmitters.
- ➤ This will stimulate the synapse even in the absence of the normal neurotransmitter.
- ➤ Other types of chemical act as inhibitors.
- ➤ An inhibitor molecule will bind to the postsynaptic receptor but not cause depolarisation.
- ➤ The normal neurotransmitter cannot bind so no postsynaptic impulse occurs.
- ➤ Example – neonicotinoid pesticide binds to acetyl choline receptors.

1. What is the name given to the layer of cells covering the neuron?	2. What is the name of the gaps between these cells?	3. Does the sodium-potassium pump transport sodium ions into or out of the axoplasm?
4. What is the approximate potential difference at the resting potential?	5. What is the name given to the potential difference that has to be reached before an action potential occurs?	6a. Name the two phases of an action potential?
6b. What causes the first of these two phases to occur?	6c. What causes the second of these two phases to occur?	7. How is the diffusion of sodium ions controlled?
8. In a myelinated neuron the impulse jumps from gap to gap. What is the name for this type of conduction?	9. Are vesicles of neurotransmitter released from the pre- or post-synaptic membrane?	10. What causes neurotransmitter to be released?
11a. What does the neurotransmitter do when it reaches the other side of the synaptic gap?	11b. What does this cause?	12. State two consequences of a chemical mimicking a neurotransmitter.

The endocrine system

The endocrine system

This is the second of the two systems that control the body. It consists of many glands distributed around the body. These glands secrete chemicals called hormones directly into the blood stream and the hormones circulate in the blood and stimulate specific cells. Only certain cells will respond to the circulating hormone. These cells have receptors – glycoproteins – for the particular hormone on their plasma membrane.

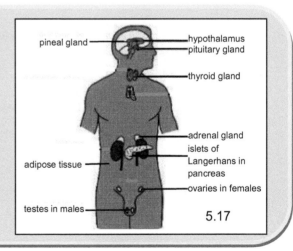

pineal gland — hypothalamus / pituitary gland
thyroid gland
adrenal gland
islets of Langerhans in pancreas
adipose tissue
ovaries in females
testes in males

5.17

Homeostasis

Key point

➢ Homeostasis is maintaining the internal environment between narrow limits –
  - blood pH,
  - carbon dioxide concentration,
  - blood glucose concentration,
  - body temperature,
  - water balance.

Principles

➢ Receptor or sensor monitors level of variable.
➢ Co-ordinating centre regulates level of variable.
➢ Effectors bring about the changes directed by the co-ordinating centre.
➢ The process is called **negative feedback**.
➢ The endocrine and nervous systems are both involved in homeostasis.

Negative feedback

Principle

➢ When a variable deviates from the norm the result of the effector mechanisms is to return the variable back to the norm.

Graph showing the process of negative feedback

Control of blood glucose

Change in blood sugar level detected by islet cells in pancreas

Increase

Decrease

Beta cells in pancreas secrete insulin

Alpha cells in pancreas secrete glucagon

Blood glucose lowered by:
1. Increased uptake into cells.
2. Increased conversion to glycogen in muscles and liver.
3. Increased conversion to fat in adipose tissue.
4. Increased rate of respiration.

Blood glucose raised by:
1. Increased breakdown of liver glycogen, (not muscle glycogen).
2. Synthesis of glucose from fats and amino acids (gluconeogenesis)

Islets in the pancreas

5.18 Section through a pancreas

Tip – You are studying the IB course – Insulin --- **B**eta cells.	Warning – take care not to confuse glycogen and glucagon. Glucag**on** is the horm**one**.

IBSL Biology 2016 © Ashby Merson-Davies

Diabetes

Key facts

- Diabetes is failure to control blood glucose level leading to abnormally high levels of glucose in the blood (hyperglycaemia).
- The kidney threshold* is exceeded and glucose is excreted.
- Urine volume increases causing thirst.
- Muscle tissue is broken down leading to weight loss.
- Vision can be seriously damaged (retinopathy).
- Kidney failure may occur.

> * When the kidney first filters the blood glucose is found in this filtrate. However it is normally all reabsorbed back into the blood. The threshold is the maximum level of glucose in the filtrate that can all be reabsorbed.

Type I (early onset or juvenile) diabetes

- Usually starts early in life, often very suddenly.
- Due to loss of insulin secreting cells in the pancreas.
- Controlled by testing level of blood sugar and then injecting an appropriate quantity of insulin.
- Control has to continue throughout life.
- Potential for stem cell therapy – see blue box.

> In October 2014 stem cell researchers at Harvard University announced a breakthrough in the production of human beta cells from embryonic stem cells – see page 56. Trials in animal models, including non-human primates, are being conducted along with methods of protecting the cells from attack by the immune system.

Type II (late onset) diabetes

- Comes on gradually, usually in late middle age.
- Commonly associated with being overweight for a long time.
- Persistent over-eating of sugary foods causes high levels of plasma insulin.
- This reduces the sensitivity of the insulin target cells so they fail to take up sufficient glucose from the blood.
- Often controlled by reducing carbohydrate intake which allows the target cells to recover.
- Controlled by eating a healthy diet high in fibre and complex carbohydrates – beans, lentils, pulses and wholegrain cereals and low in saturated fats and salt. Sugary and fatty snack foods and sugary drinks should be avoided.

Control of metabolic rate and temperature

Key points

- Thyroxin is secreted by the thyroid gland.
- Its release is regulated by a hormonal pathway controlled by the hypothalamus in the brain.
- Thyroxin controls the metabolic rate and is essential for proper growth and development, both physical and mental.
- Prolonged exposure to cold will stimulate the hypothalamus to release more thyroxin to increase the metabolic rate.
- A side product of metabolism is heat.

Control of appetite

Key points

- Leptin is one of several hormones involved in energy homeostasis.
- It regulates the amount of fat stored in the body.
- It is secreted by cells in adipose (fat) tissue.
- It is secreted when the adipose tissue reaches a particular level and acts on the hypothalamus to inhibit appetite and increase metabolism.

Clinical obesity

➤ Clinical obesity is when a person has been diagnosed as obese by a doctor.

➤ They have a BMI of over 30kg m^{-2}.

➤ Obese patients generally have a higher level of plasma leptin than a non-obese person.

➤ This is contrary to expectation.

➤ One hypothesis is that there is a fault with the leptin signalling system in the cells of the hypothalamus.

➤ Hence injections of leptin to try and reduce hunger feelings are unsuccessful.

Control of circadian rhythms

Key points

➤ Several aspects of the body have circadian rhythms, e.g. hormone release, temperature.

➤ The most obvious one is the sleep-wake cycle.

➤ The 'master' clock for the body is a group of cells (called the SCN) in the hypothalamus.

➤ The sleep-wake cycle is controlled by the hormone melatonin.

➤ Melatonin is secreted by the pineal gland in the brain.

➤ Secretion follows a regular pattern of high during the night and low during the day.

➤ It is broken down rapidly by the liver so blood concentrations rise and fall sharply.

➤ The pattern is maintained by the natural light – dark cycle.

➤ A special type of ganglion cell in the retina detects light at wavelength around 470nm (blue light) and sends signals to the SCN to maintain the rhythm.

➤ Melatonin stimulates the sleep part of the cycle.

➤ In teenagers melatonin secretion follows a cycle to the right of the adult pattern, making them wakeful during the evening and sleepy in the morning.

Circadian rhythm

This is a daily physical, mental or behavioural rhythm based on the 24 hour light/dark cycle and is shown by a very wide variety of organisms – animals, plants and fungi. The clock is a cellular mechanism and is largely independent from the light /dark cycle, the organism continues to show the circadian rhythm even when the light/dark pattern is changed. Repeated behaviour contrary to the natural circadian rhythm, e.g. night-time shift work, can lead to ill

Jet lag

➤ This is caused by rapid travel across time zones.

➤ Moving to a different time zone disrupts the natural circadian rhythm.

➤ Over a period of time the brain resets to the new rhythm.

➤ The greater the number of time zones crossed the longer it takes for the brain to reset.

➤ Melatonin tablets can be used to alleviate it – see blue box.

Use of melatonin

Melatonin tablets can be bought over the counter in many countries or online, but in some countries they are not approved for sale. Like all drugs, they are open to misuse and their efficacy is not proven since dosage and timing are highly variable.

1. What is the name given to the process of maintaining a constant internal environment?	2. What is the name given to the regulatory pathway for this process?	3. State two examples excluding control of blood sugar.
4. Which pancreatic cells produce glucagon?	5. What is the most common cause of type II diabetes?	6. Name the hormone used to control metabolic rate.
7a. Name the hormone used to control appetite.	7b. What does this hormone measure in order to do this?	8. What is the minimum BMI for a person to be classed as obese?
9. What is the name given to daily rhythms such as the sleep-wake cycle?	10. Name the hormone used to regulate the sleep-wake cycle?	11. Is this hormone secreted in the dark or light?

 IBSL Biology 2016 © Ashby Merson-Davies

Reproduction

oviduct
- picks up secondary oocyte at ovulation.
- site of fertilisation.
- transports blastocyst to uterus

ovary
- releases (usually) one secondary oocyte once a month.
- releases progesterone and Oestrogen during pregnancy

uterus
- place where the fetus grows

endometrium
- lining which breaks down and is replaced each month. When the blastocyst reaches the uterus it sinks into the endometrium

pubic bone

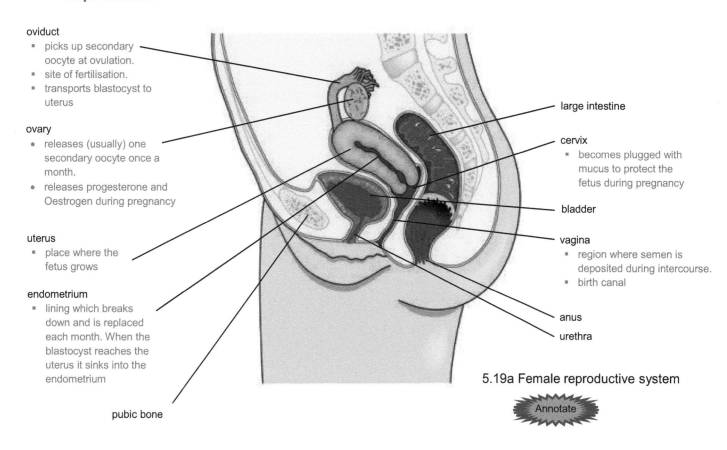

large intestine

cervix
- becomes plugged with mucus to protect the fetus during pregnancy

bladder

vagina
- region where semen is deposited during intercourse.
- birth canal

anus

urethra

5.19a Female reproductive system

Annotate

erectile tissue
- fills with blood to produce an erection

penis
- enters vagina to release semen near cervix during ejaculation

urethra – transports
- urine.
- semen during an ejaculation

vas deferens / sperm duct
- transfers sperm during ejaculation

testis – produces
- sperm.
- testosterone

scrotal sac / scrotum
- keeps testes at a lower temperature

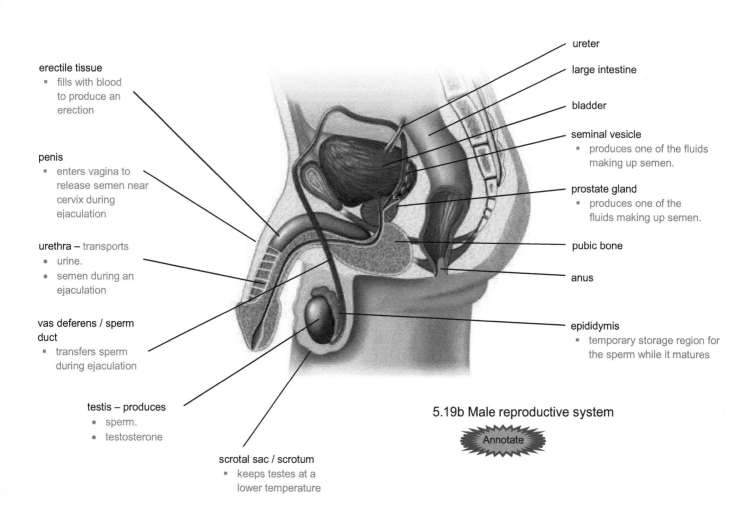

ureter

large intestine

bladder

seminal vesicle
- produces one of the fluids making up semen.

prostate gland
- produces one of the fluids making up semen.

pubic bone

anus

epididymis
- temporary storage region for the sperm while it matures

5.19b Male reproductive system

Annotate

Reproductive hormones

- During early fetal development both male and female gonads develop close to the kidney and the male external genitalia look like that of a female.
- A gene on the Y chromosome causes the gonads in the male embryo to develop as testes and to move down through the abdominal cavity into the scrotal sac.
- The testes start to produce testosterone and this causes the external genitalia to develop into the male structures.

Hormone	Function	
	Boys	**Girls**
Testosterone	• Pre-natal development of genitalia. • Development of secondary sexual characteristics. • Stimulates final stages of spermatogenesis. • Maintains the sex drive.	
Oestrogen		• Pre-natal development of genitalia. • Development of secondary sexual characteristics.
Follicle stimulating hormone (FSH)		• Causes one or more follicles in the ovaries to mature. • Stimulates secretion of oestrogen.
Luteinising hormone (LH)		• Stimulates ovulation. • Stimulates conversion of empty follicle into corpus luteum. • Stimulates secretion of progesterone.
Oestrogen		• Initiates repair of uterus lining. • Positive feedback on LH to trigger ovulation.
Progesterone		• Completes repair of uterus lining. • Negative feedback on pituitary to block release of FSH. • Maintains uterus lining in early part of pregnancy.

The menstrual cycle

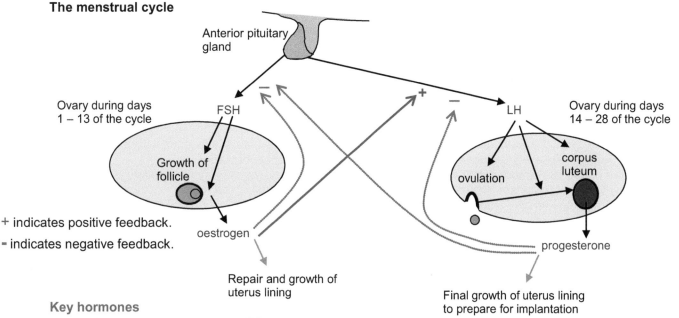

Anterior pituitary gland

Ovary during days 1 – 13 of the cycle

FSH

Growth of follicle

Ovary during days 14 – 28 of the cycle

LH

ovulation

corpus luteum

+ indicates positive feedback.

- indicates negative feedback.

oestrogen

Repair and growth of uterus lining

progesterone

Final growth of uterus lining to prepare for implantation

Key hormones
➢ Follicle stimulating hormone, FSH.
➢ Oestrogen.
➢ Luteinising hormone, LH.
➢ Progesterone.

Order of release

Note – the number of bullet points corresponds to the number of arrows from each hormone on the diagram above.

Link these steps to both the diagram above and to the levels of hormones on the graphs below.

Key steps
➢ FSH released from anterior pituitary.
  • stimulates growth of follicle,
  • stimulates secretion of oestrogen.
➢ Oestrogen released from follicle cells.
  • initiates repair and growth of endometrium (uterus lining),
  • negative feedback on pituitary to block FSH release,
  • nearing middle of cycle it reaches a critical level which causes a positive feedback on pituitary to release LH.
➢ LH released from anterior pituitary.
  • stimulates ovulation through a positive feedback mechanism – hence the sharp peak,
  • stimulates conversion of empty follicle to corpus luteum,
  • stimulates secretion of oestrogen and progesterone by corpus luteum.
➢ Progesterone released from corpus luteum.
  • completes growth of endometrium,
  • negative feedback on pituitary blocking FSH,
  • negative feedback on pituitary blocking LH.

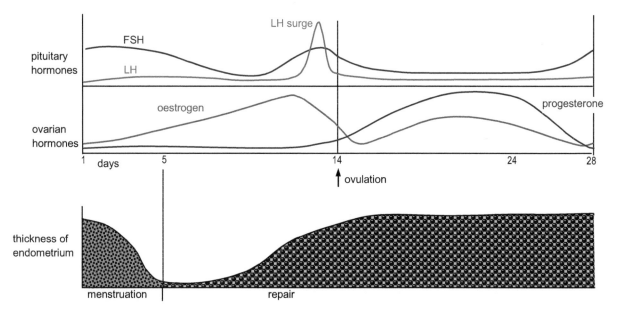

IVF – *in vitro* fertilisation

Key steps
➢ A drug is injected daily for about 2/3 weeks to stop the normal menstrual cycle.
➢ FSH is then injected daily for about 12 days in order to induce development of several follicles in the ovaries.
➢ HCG is then injected to cause the follicles to mature.
➢ About 35 hours later eggs from the mature follicles in both ovaries are collected by a tube inserted via the vagina.
➢ The eggs are transferred to a dish of warmed physiological saline and the sperms from the man added.
➢ After about 20 hours incubation the eggs are checked to see if fertilisation has occurred.
➢ After 1 – 5 days the embryos are examined for any signs of abnormalities.
➢ If necessary a more detailed genetic check can be carried out by karyotyping and/or gene probes.
➢ Hormonal treatment, progesterone or hCG, prepares the mother's uterus.
➢ A selected embryo is then inserted into the mother's uterus. Usually this is a single embryo but under certain circumstances two may be inserted.

William Harvey and sexual reproduction in deer
(1578 – 1657)
➢ Harvey investigated human circulation.
➢ He also investigated sexual reproduction.
➢ The prevailing idea at the time was that an embryo was a fully formed organism but in miniature form and it simply grew.
➢ Harvey first observed growth in fertilised hens' eggs as these were large and easy to obtain and observe.
➢ He saw that a simple drop of blood on the surface of the yolk would grow into the new chick and this led him to disagree with the preformed idea.

5.20 Roe deer

➢ He repeated his observations many times to provide sufficient evidence.
➢ Observing deer he noticed that offspring appeared only after mating.
➢ He examined the uteruses of female deer during the mating season but only found a developing embryo two or more months after mating.
➢ Since he did not have a microscope he was unable to observe the early stages of development and therefore wrongly concluded that the male 'seed' was of no importance.
➢ Microscopes had been invented in the 1590s but were not widely known about.
➢ In 1677 Anton van Leeuwenhoek, a Dutch draper and amateur scientist, used powerful lenses and a simple microscope that he had made to observe sperm in semen.

Glossary

Cancer	Uncontrolled mitosis resulting in a tumour.
Effector	A gland or muscle which responds to a stimulus.
Emulsify	Breaking large fat droplets into much smaller droplets to increase surface area for digestion.
Epithelium	A layer of cells covering the body and lining the digestive tract.
Gonads	Ovaries and testes.
Occlusion	Partial or complete blockage of a blood vessel.
Pesticide	A chemical that kills pests.
Positive feedback	A response where the output feeds back in to further increase the output.
Pulmonary	To do with the lungs.
Selective reabsorption	A process which selects particular substances to be reabsorbed.
Surfactant	A chemical which lowers surface tension.
Systemic	To do with the body.
Variable	A factor which changes.
Ventilation	Moving air or water over the gas exchange surfaces.

1. What is the name of the lining of the uterus?	2a. Name the hormone that results in development of the secondary sexual characteristics in boys.	2b. On which chromosome is the gene found that results in the production of this hormone?
3. Name the hormone that results in development of the secondary sexual characteristics in girls.	4. Name the hormone that stimulates the secretion of oestrogen in the menstrual cycle.	5. Which part of the ovary produces oestrogen?
6a. List the two reproductive hormones released from the pituitary gland.	6b. Are they released from the anterior or posterior part of the pituitary?	7a. Name the hormone that maintains the uterus lining for the first few weeks of pregnancy.
7b. Name the structure in the ovary that secretes this hormone.	8. Name the hormone that causes ovulation.	9. What type of feedback does oestrogen have on the release of FSH?

Answers to Grey Box Questions   **Underlined words are required.**

The human gut

1. Store bile.
2. Very acidic; destroys pathogens; starts protein digestion.
3. Alkaline.
4. Main digestive region; main absorptive region.
5. Absorb water; large numbers of bacteria.
6. Neutralise stomach acid; emulsify fats.
7. Amylase; lipase.
8. Break down / hydrolyse proteins.
9. Amylase.
10. Maltase.
11. On the (outer) plasma membrane of the villus cells.
12. Active transport.
13. Liver.
14. Large molecules cannot be absorbed; so that the body can build its own large molecules from the monomers.
15. Because the digestion reactions are too slow at body temperature.
16. Duodenum; ileum.
17. Peristalsis.
18. longitudinal and circular.
19. Finger-like shape to give large surface area; surface cells with microvilli to increase surface area; surface cells with large numbers of mitochondria for active transport; capillary network; lacteal.
20. Duodenum.
21. Cellulose.

Gas exchange

1. Type I and type II pneumocytes.
2. Type I – very thin for gas exchange;
    Type II – produce a surfactant.
3. To maintain a high concentration gradient between the alveolar air and the blood.
4. Decreases.
5. Diaphragm; external intercostal muscles.
6. Abdominal muscles; internal intercostal muscles.
7. Antagonistic.
8. Tidal volume.
9. Number of breaths per minute.
10. See page 111.
11. Smoking.
12. Uncontrolled cell division.
13. Removal of a lung; death.
14. Smoking.
15. Breakdown of the alveolar walls.
16. Difficulty in breathing; requiring an oxygen mask.

The blood system

1. Blood passes through the heart twice for each circuit.
2. Right.
3. Systemic.
4. Coronary artery.
5. Liver.
6. Arteries.
7. Pulmonary vein.
8. Aorta.
9. Atrioventricular valve.
10. Semi lunar.
11. Left ventricle.
12. Right atrium.
13a. Sinoatrial node.
13b. Wall of the right atrium.
13c. It releases electrical pulses to control the basic heart rate.
13d. Medulla / cardiac control centre of the brain.
13e. To speed up and slow down the basic heart rate.
14. Epinephrine.
15. Adrenal.
16. Maintain a one-way flow.
17. Systole.
18.a. Contraction of the left ventricle.
18b. Contraction of the left ventricle.
18c. Relaxation of the left ventricle.
19. Plaque / fatty deposit in the artery wall.
20. Angina / heart attack.
21. Vein.
22. To maintain blood flow when the ventricles realax.
23. Collagen.
24. When they contract blood pressure and hence flow rate increase.
25. Single celled wall; cells are flattened.

Defence against infectious disease

1. An organism or virus that causes disease.
2. Antibiotics work on specific prokaryotic metabolic pathways; viruses use the eukaryotic host metabolic pathway so an antibiotic would damage the cell.
3. Penicillin could be used to destroy pathogenic bacteria with harming the patient.
4. Skin; mucus membranes.
5a. Damaged blood vessels; exposure to air.   5b. Platelets.   5c. Thrombin.
6. Phagocyte.
7. Antigen – a molecule foreign to the body that stimulates an immune response.
   Antibody – a specific protein made by lymphocytes in response to a specific antigen and helps to destroy the antigen.
8a. Helper T lymphocyte.
8b. The antibody producing cells cannot be activated.
9. Unprotected vaginal or anal intercourse; oral sex; across the placenta; breast feeding; during birth; contaminated needles; blood transfusion.

The nervous system

1. Myelin sheath cells (Schwann cells).   2.   Nodes of Ranvier.
3. Out of.   4.   -70mv (Must state units).   5.   Threshold.
6a. Depolarisation; repolarisation.   6b.   Diffusion of sodium ions into the axoplasm.
6c. Diffusion of potassium ions out of the axoplasm and active transport of sodium ions out of the axoplasm.
7. By voltage gated channels.   8.   Saltatory.   9.   Presysnaptic membrane.
10. Calcium ions.   11a. Binds to a receptor.
11b. Diffusion of sodium ions into the post-synaptic neuron / depolarisation of the post-synaptic neuron.
12. i. It can block the binding of the normal neurotransmitter.
    ii. It can stimulate a post-synaptic potential.

The endocrine system

1. Homeostasis.   2.   Blood pH; body temperature; blood concentration.
3. Negative feedback.   4.   Alpha.   5.   Over-weight / eating too many sugary foods.
6. Thyroxin.   7a.   Leptin.   7b.   Amount of stored fat.
8. 30kg m^{-2} (must state units)   9.   Circadian rhythms.
10. Melatonin.   11.   Dark.

Reproduction.

1. Endometrium.   2a. Testosterone   2b. Y chromosome.
3. Oestrogen   4.   Follicle stimulating hormone.   5.   Follicle cells.
6a. Follicle stimulating hormone and luteinising hormone.   6b. Anterior.
7a. Progesterone.   7b. Corpus luteum   8. Luteinising hormone.
9. Negative.

Self-test Quizzes

Digestion and absorption

1. Which of the following is the correct sequence for the gut structures?
   a. Mouth, stomach, oesophagus, small intestine, large intestine,
   b. Mouth, oesophagus, stomach, large intestine, small intestine,
   c. Mouth, oesophagus, stomach, small intestine, large intestine,
   d. Mouth, stomach, small intestine, large intestine, oesophagus.

2. Digestion is necessary because:
   a. large food molecules cannot be absorbed through the intestine wall,
   b. this makes the food more nutritious,
   c. it changes the pH so the food molecules can be absorbed,
   d. only large food molecules can be taken up by phagocytosis.

3. The finger-like shape of a villus is so that:
   a. the surface area is increased for absorption,
   b. it is able to move food along the intestine,
   c. it protects the absorptive surface of the intestine,
   d. it helps to break up the large pieces of food.

4. Assimilation is:
   a. absorption of digested food,
   b. use of absorbed food by the body,
   c. removal of undigested food from the body,
   d. absorption of gases through the alveoli.

5. Which of the following statements about bile is correct?
   a. It contains enzymes that digest all three food groups.
   b. It has a low pH to kill microbes.
   c. It has a high pH to emulsify fats.
   d. It is alkaline to neutralise stomach acid.

6. Which types of enzyme are found in the human digestive system?

         i. Amylases   ii. Proteases   iii. Nucleases

   a. i and ii only,
   b. i and iii only,
   c. ii and iii only,
   d. i, ii and iii.

7. Assimilation and absorption both occur in the body. What is required for assimilation but is not required for absorption?
   a. enzymes to synthesize new molecules,
   b. active transport mechanisms,
   c. dissolved nutrients,
   d. diffusion gradient.

8. Where in the body is the gall bladder located?
   a. in the neck,
   b. in the liver,
   c. beside the pancreas,
   d. above the small intestine.

9. What does the digestion of starch by pancreatic amylase produce?
    a. glucose,
    b. maltose,
    c. amylos,
    d. amylopectin.

Gas Exchange

1. Which of the following is the correct sequence as air flows into the lungs?
    a. trachea – bronchus – bronchioles – alveoli,
    b. trachea – bronchioles – bronchi – alveoli,
    c. bronchi – bronchioles – trachea – alveoli,
    d. trachea – alveoli – bronchi – bronchioles.

2. Which of the following is **not** part of the process of ventilation?
    a. The volume of the thoracic cavity changes.
    b. The pressure in the thoracic cavity changes.
    c. Gas exchange occurs between alveolar air and blood.
    d. The diaphragm muscle contracts.

3. How many plasma membranes are between alveolar air and haemoglobin in a red blood cell?
    a. Two,
    b. Three,
    c. Four,
    d. Five.

4. Which of the following is the function of type I pneumocytes?
    a. production of surfactant,
    b. form the capillary wall,
    c. very thin to promote gas exchange,
    d. contain contractile fibres to squeeze air out of the alveoli.

5. Which of the following statements about breathing in is correct?
    a. External intercostal muscles and diaphragm muscles contract.
    b. Internal intercostal and abdominal muscles contract.
    c. External intercostal muscles and abdominal muscles contract.
    d. Internal intercostal muscles contract and abdominal muscles relax.

6. Tidal volume is:
    a. the volume of air breathed in during one minute,
    b. the difference in the volume of air breathed in when at rest and when exercising,
    c. the volume of air breathed in and out during one minute,
    d. the volume of air breathed in and out during a single breath.

7. Which of the following statements about emphysema is correct?
    a. It is caused by strenuous exercise.
    b. It is a reduction in the surface area of the alveoli.
    c. It is due to the loss of the surfactant-producing pneumocytes.
    d. The alveolar walls break down due to a loss of capillaries.

8. Ventilation is necessary because it:
   a. regulates water vapour loss from the body,
   b. increases the loss of oxygen from the red blood cells,
   c. allows the abdominal muscles to move,
   d. maintains concentration gradients of gases between alveoli and blood.

The blood system

1. Which line in the table below shows correctly the type of blood in the vessel?

	Coronary artery	Pulmonary artery	Vena cava	Pulmonary vein
a.	oxygenated	oxygenated	deoxygenated	deoxygenated
b.	oxygenated	deoxygenated	oxygenated	deoxygenated
c.	deoxygenated	oxygenated	deoxygenated	deoxygenated
d.	oxygenated	deoxygenated	deoxygenated	oxygenated

2. Which line in the table below shows correctly the description for the blood vessels?

	Artery	Capillary	Vein
a.	Large lumen	Thin layer of muscle	Valves
b.	Thin layer of muscle	Valves	Large lumen
c.	Thick layer of muscle	Wall one cell thick	Valves
d.	Thick layer of muscle	Valves	Thin layer of muscle

3. Which of the following statements is correct?
   a. When the ventricles contract the semilunar valves are closed.
   b. When the atria contract the atrio-ventricular valves are closed.
   c. When the atria contract the semilunar valves are opened.
   d. When the ventricles contract the atrio-ventricular valves are closed.

4. The hormone that affects heart rate is:
   a. adrenalin,
   b. thyroxin,
   c. insulin,
   d. glucagon.

5. The right ventricle pumps blood into the:
   a. pulmonary vein,
   b. pulmonary artery,
   c. aorta,
   d. coronary artery.

6. Which of the following heart chambers contain oxygenated blood?
   a. right atrium and left atrium,
   b. left ventricle and right ventricle,
   c. left atrium and left ventricle,
   d. right ventricle and right atrium.

7. What is the cause of the semilunar valves closing?
   a. contraction of the ventricles,
   b. contraction of the atria,
   c. relaxation of the ventricles,
   d. relaxation of the atria.

8. In which heart chamber is the SAN found?
   a. right atrium,
   b. right ventricle,
   c. left atrium,
   d. left ventricle.

9. Two nerves are connected to the SAN. Which statement about these nerves is correct?
   a. They carry sensory impulses to the brain to monitor heart rate.
   b. They are connected to the medulla of the brain.
   c. One is a sensory nerve and the other is a motor nerve.
   d. Their nerve impulses maintain a steady heart rate during times of stress.

10. During systole of the left ventricle which of the following statements is correct?
    a. The semilunar valves are closed.
    b. The blood pressure in the aorta is falling.
    c. The atrioventricular valve is open.
    d. The blood pressure in the ventricle is rising.

11. Which of the following statements about the valves in the heart is correct?
    a. They ensure a one-way flow of blood through the heart.
    b. They prevent the oxygenated and deoxygenated blood from mixing.
    c. The help to pump the blood from the atria to the ventricles.
    d. They direct the flow of blood into the correct arteries.

12. Which of the following is a function of the collagen fibres in the artery wall?
    a. They prevent the wall from overstretching when the ventricles contract.
    b. They are elastic and so help maintain the blood flow between ventricular contractions.
    c. They can contract to assist in the pumping of the blood.
    d. They are very smooth which helps with the flow of blood through the artery.

13. Which of the following blood vessels have a large lumen relative to their diameter?
    a. arteries only,
    b. capillaries,
    c. both arteries and veins,
    d. veins only.

14. Which one of the following statements about the liver is correct?
    a. It receives blood only through an artery.
    b. It receives blood through an artery and a vein from the gut.
    c. Blood leaving the liver passes to the gut via a vein.
    d. The liver has a double arterial supply.

15. The pacemaker is:
    a. the region of the heart that regulates the rate of heart beat,
    b. the region of the brain that regulates the rate of heart beat,
    c. the region of the brain that regulates the rate of breathing,
    d. the nerves from the brain that affect the heart rate.

Defence against infectious diseases

1. Viruses are not organisms because:
    a. they are too small,
    b. they do not possess a nucleus,
    c. their ribosomes are a different size from prokaryotic ribosomes,
    d. they are not considered to be living.

2. Which of the following happens during the clotting process?
    a. Platelets in the plasma release fibrin when exposed to air.
    b. Fibrinogen in the plasma stimulates the release of clotting factors.
    c. Clotting factors from platelets convert prothrombin to thrombin.
    d. Macrophages release thrombin which results in the formation of fibrin fibres in the blood.

3. Which of the following statements about antibiotics is correct?
    a. They act against specific chemical pathways found only in prokaryotes.
    b. They act against specific chemical pathways found only in eukaryotes.
    c. They are specific proteins produced by the body in response to an antigen.
    d. They are chemicals produce by lymphocytes to help fight pathogens.

4. Which of the following statements is correct?
    a. Antibodies are proteins made by red blood cells.
    b. Antigens are molecules made by white blood cells.
    c. Antibodies are proteins that can destroy antigens.
    d. Antigens are proteins that can destroy antibodies.

5. A pathogen may be defined as:
    a. a form of vaccine that is used to stimulate a defensive response,
    b. a type of white blood cell that fights infection,
    c. an organism or virus that causes disease,
    d. a bacterial population o or in the body.

6. Which of the following statements about HIV is correct?
    a. It is a virus which destroys helper T lymphocytes.
    b. It is a bacterium which invades the antibody-producing cells.
    c. It causes AIDS by invading many different types of body cell, especially the lungs.
    d. It prevents lymphocytes from producing antibodies by binding to the lymphocyte antigen.

                                                    IBSL Biology 2016 © Ashby Merson-Davies

The nervous system

1. The nodes of Ranvier are found:
    a. at the ends of motor neurons,
    b. between myelin sheath cells,
    c. around the cell body of a motor neuron,
    d. between two neurons.

2. During the resting potential which of the following statements is true?
    a. Potassium ions are pumped out of the axoplasm.
    b. Potassium ions diffuse into the axoplasm.
    c. Sodium ions diffuse into the axoplasm.
    d. Potassium ions diffuse out of the axoplasm.

3. Which of the following ions initiates an action potential?
    a. potassium,
    b. calcium,
    c. sodium,
    d. phosphate.

4. During the recovery phase of an action potential:
    a. gated channels open to increase the flow of potassium ions out of the axoplasm,
    b. gated channels open to increase the flow of sodium ions out of the axoplasm,
    c. the sodium-potassium pump reverses direction,
    d. potassium ions are pumped out of the axoplasm.

5. During transmission of a nerve impulse along an axon which of the following events happens?
    a. Sodium ions diffuse into the axon and potassium ions diffuse out.
    b. Potassium ions diffuse into the axon and sodium ions diffuse out.
    c. Potassium ions are pumped into the axon and sodium ions diffuse out.
    d. Sodium ions are pumped into the axon and potassium ions diffuse out.

6. Which of the following occurs during transmission across a synapse?
    a. Vesicles of neurotransmitter bind to the post-synaptic membrane.
    b. The incoming nerve impulse opens gated sodium channels causing depolarisation.
    c. The incoming nerve impulse causes sodium ions to diffuse across the synaptic gap.
    d. Neurotransmitter diffuses through the post-synaptic membrane causing depolarisation.

7. Which of the following statements about synapses is correct?
    a. Diffusion of potassium ions through the post-synaptic membrane causes depolarisation.
    b. Acetyl choline acts as a synaptic inhibitor in insects.
    c. Acetic acid and choline are released from vesicles in the pre-synaptic membrane and form acetyl choline in the synaptic gap.
    d. Binding of neurotransmitter to a receptor on the post-synaptic membrane causes gated sodium channels to open.

8. Neonicotinoids pesticides are synaptic inhibitors. They work by:
    a. preventing the binding of neurotransmitter vesicles to the presynaptic membrane,
    b. binding to the acetylcholine receptor on the postsynaptic membrane,
    c. inhibiting the catalysis of acetylcholine by cholinesterase,
    d. preventing sodium ions diffusing through the postsynaptic membrane.

The endocrine system

1. Homeostasis can be described as:
    a.   maintaining a constant internal environment,
    b.   blood clotting,
    c.   maintaining a steady breathing rate,
    d.   maintaining a constant weight.

2. Negative feedback can be described as:
    a.   ejection of the contents of the stomach through the mouth,
    b.   changing the level of a variable to suit the demands of the body,
    c.   a mechanism that corrects a change in the level of a variable,
    d.   monitoring the level of a variable.

3. The diagram shows how the body regulates the level of glucose in the blood.

    What are P and Q?

	P	Q
a.	Glucagon	Insulin
b.	Insulin	Glycogen
c.	Glycogen	Thyroxin
d.	Insulin	Glucagon

4. Which cells secrete insulin?
    a.   α cells of the pancreas,
    b.   β cells of the pancreas,
    c.   β cells of the liver,
    d.   Epithelial cells of the small intestine.

5. Early onset or Type I diabetes is due to:
    a.   loss of insulin secreting cells,
    b.   persistent over-eating of sugary foods,
    c.   failure of liver cells to remove glucose from the blood,
    d.   over-production of insulin.

6. Which of the following lines in the table is correct?

	Thyroxin	Leptin	Melatonin
a.	Helps maintain body temperature.	Helps control appetite.	Causes pigmentation of the skin.
b.	Helps control appetite.	Helps maintain body temperature.	Controls the sleep-wake pattern.
c.	Helps maintain body temperature.	Helps control appetite.	Controls the sleep-wake pattern.
d.	Controls the sleep-wake pattern.	Helps control appetite.	Helps maintain body temperature.

7. Which of the following structures secretes melatonin?
   a. pituitary gland,
   b. hypothalamus,
   c. pineal gland,
   d. thyroid gland.

Reproduction

1. In the male reproductive system:
   a. the epididymis assists in sperm production,
   b. the urethra can transport both urine and semen,
   c. the seminal vesicles are temporary storage places while the sperm mature,
   d. the vas deferens carries urine from the bladder to the outside.

2. In the female reproductive system:
   a. the urethra can transport both urine and oocytes,
   b. the oviducts join the uterus next to the cervix,
   c. the lining of the uterus is called the endometrium,
   d. the cervix connects the oviducts to the uterus.

3. The hormone that causes the pre-natal development of the genitalia in girls is:
   a. Oestrogen,
   b. progesterone,
   c. luteinising hormone,
   d. follicle stimulating hormone.

4. Testosterone is produced by the:
   a. seminal vesicles,
   b. prostate gland,
   c. specialised cells in the testes,
   d. epididymis.

5. Which of these structures produces progesterone?
   a. anterior pituitary gland,
   b. posterior pituitary gland,
   c. follicle,
   d. corpus luteum.

6. In the menstrual cycle:
   a. the follicle produces the hormone Oestrogen,
   b. growth of the follicle is stimulated by Oestrogen,
   c. follicle stimulating hormone has a negative feedback on the pituitary gland,
   d. Oestrogen causes the endometrium to break down.

7. In the menstrual cycle:
   a. ovulation is stimulated by a surge in luteinising hormone,
   b. progesterone from the corpus luteum initiates the repair of the uterus lining,
   c. Oestrogen stimulates the conversion of the empty follicle into the corpus luteum,
   d. progesterone has a positive feedback on the pituitary gland to stimulate the release of luteinising hormone.

8. During IVF treatment:
   a. LH is injected to stimulate multiple ovulation,
   b. FSH is injected to regulate the menstrual cycle,
   c. FSH is injected to stimulate growth of several follicles,
   d. progesterone is injected to stimulate growth of several follicles.

Chapter Six

Ecology

Ecology is the study of the environment – species, communities, and all the ways they interact with each other and their non-living (abiotic) environment. Since the human species is having a major, sometimes catastrophic, impact on our planet, the study of ecology becomes increasingly important. Global warming, deforestation and ocean acidification are just three of the important issues.

Species, communities and ecosystems

Species

- ➤ Species are groups of organisms that can potentially interbreed to produce fertile offspring.
- ➤ Members of a species may be reproductively isolated in separate populations.

Example – Ramshorn snails living in one pond may have the potential to breed with the Ramshorn snails living in a nearby pond but are isolated from them by the dry land between the ponds.

Sometimes different species can interbreed but the offspring are infertile. Example – a mule is a horse × donkey.

6.1 A mule

Population

- ➤ This is a group of organisms of the same species living in the same place.

Community

- ➤ This is formed by populations of different species living together and interacting with each other.

You need to know how to use the chi-squared test on data collected from random sampling. Revise Chapter One, page 9.

Ecosystem

- ➤ This is formed by the interaction of a community with its abiotic environment.

Ways of feeding

Autotroph – an organism that synthesises its organic molecules from simple inorganic substances which are obtained from the abiotic environment.

6.2 Wild flowers

Heterotroph – an organism that obtains organic molecules from other organisms.

6.3 Hyena, Tanzania

Saprotroph – a heterotrophic organism that lives on or in non-living organic matter, secreting digestive enzymes onto it and absorbing the products of digestion.

6.4 Fungi on a rotting log

Consumer – a heterotrophic organism that ingests other organic matter that is living or recently killed.

Detritivore – a heterotrophic organism that ingests detritus.

6.5 Giant millipede, Borneo

Saprotrophs and detritivores are **decomposers.**

Food chains
Key points

- ➤ A food chain shows a linear relationship of one organism feeding on another.
- ➤ Each organism is on a particular feeding or **trophic level** depending on what it is eating – see food web.
- ➤ Chemical energy in carbon compounds flows through the food chain.
- ➤ All food chains end with decomposers.

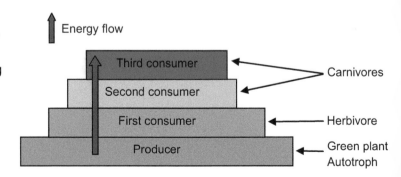

Energy flow

Third consumer	← Carnivores
Second consumer	
First consumer	← Herbivore
Producer	← Green plant Autotroph

Decomposers

➤ Animals produce faeces.
➤ All organisms may die and not be eaten by a consumer.
➤ All these organic compounds are broken down by decomposers.

6.6 Fungi growing in cow dung

Examples of food chains

A marine ecosystem:

phytoplankton ⟶ copepod ⟶ herring ⟶ tuna
(zooplankton)

A rainforest ecosystem:

fig tree fruit ⟶ vervet monkey ⟶ eagle

A freshwater lake ecosystem:

algae ⟶ tadpole ⟶ dragonfly nymph ⟶ perch ⟶ heron

Food webs

Key points
➤ A food web is a series of interlinking food chains.
➤ An omnivore is an animal that is both a herbivore and a carnivore.
➤ Omnivores and carnivores can change their feeding level depending on what they are eating.

Look at the food web below.

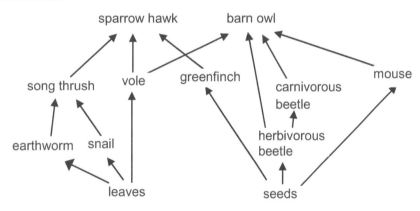

1. On the food web above deduce the feeding level of:

a. The snail. _____

b. The carnivorous beetle. _____

c. The mouse. _____

d. The sparrow hawk eating the vole. _____

e. The sparrow hawk eating the song thrush. _____

f. The barn owl eating the herbivorous beetle. _____

g. The barn owl eating the carnivorous beetle. _____

2. What is an organism that obtains organic molecules from other organisms?

3. An earthworm is eating dead leaves. What type of organism is it?

4. A fungus is feeding on dead wood. What type of organism is it?

5. What is the second level in a food chain?

6. What is a community?

Mesocosms

Key points

➢ These are small scale investigations.

➢ They are self-sustaining natural systems.

➢ They are a bridge between a controlled laboratory experiment and the more variable uncontrolled field investigation.

➢ They allow a greater number of key variables to be controlled and manipulated to evaluate how organisms or communities may respond to changing environmental conditions.

➢ They provide sufficient biological complexity relative to the natural environment being modelled.

6.7a An aquatic mesocosm

Energy flow

6.7b A rainfall mesocosm

Energy, nutrients and ecosystems

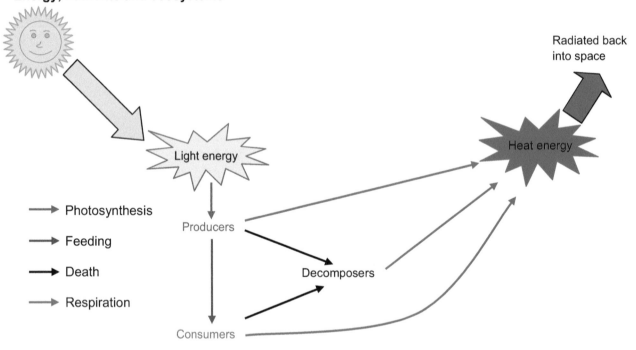

Key points – energy

➢ Energy enters most ecosystems as sunlight energy trapped by photosynthesis.

➢ Sunlight energy is continuous but variable.

➢ Photosynthesis converts the light energy to chemical energy.

➢ This chemical energy is stored in organic carbon compounds.

➢ The chemical energy in carbon compounds flows through food chains by feeding.

➢ The chemical energy is used by organisms through respiration but is converted to heat energy.

➢ As it flows through it is eventually all converted to heat energy and this leaves the ecosystem.

➢ Organisms cannot convert the heat energy to other, useable, forms of energy so it radiates into space.

The following diagram illustrates energy flow and losses in a food chain:

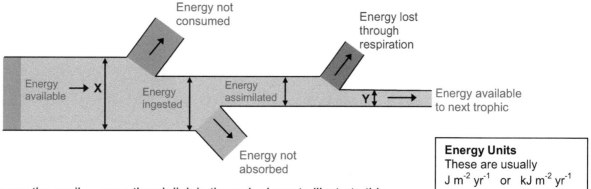

We can use the snail — song thrush link in the web above to illustrate this.

- The energy available is all the leaves in the place where the snail lives. ■
- But it will not eat all of the leaves. ■
- After digesting and absorbing some of the leaf material it has eaten some will pass out of its gut as faeces. ■
- The snail moves around and therefore uses up some of the energy it has consumed. ■
- The remainder of the energy is used for growth. This is what is available to the song thrush. ■

Efficiency of energy flow

In the diagram above the amount of energy available at the start of the trophic level is X. The amount available to the next trophic level is Y. The efficiency is best calculated as a percentage.

$$\text{Efficiency} = \frac{Y}{X} \times 100$$

Key points

➢ The efficiency of energy transfer from one trophic level to the next one is never 100%.
➢ Commonly it is 10–20%.
➢ The energy losses between trophic levels restrict the length of food chains because a point comes when there is insufficient energy available to support a further trophic level.
➢ The biomass of higher trophic levels diminishes due to the loss of carbon dioxide through respiration of organic compounds, and loss of excretory organic compounds, e.g. urea.

Pyramid of energy

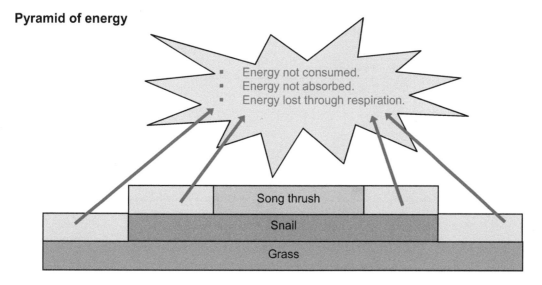

The yellow boxes represent the energy lost through a simple food chain.

Example – energy flow through a forest ecosystem:

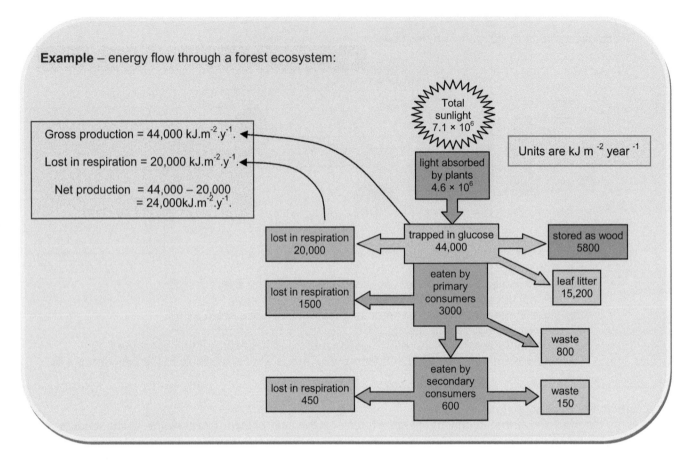

Gross production = 44,000 kJ.m^{-2}.y^{-1}.

Lost in respiration = 20,000 kJ.m^{-2}.y^{-1}.

Net production = 44,000 – 20,000
= 24,000kJ.m^{-2}.y^{-1}.

Total sunlight 7.1 × 10^6

Units are kJ m^{-2} year^{-1}

light absorbed by plants 4.6 × 10^6

lost in respiration 20,000

trapped in glucose 44,000

stored as wood 5800

leaf litter 15,200

lost in respiration 1500

eaten by primary consumers 3000

waste 800

lost in respiration 450

eaten by secondary consumers 600

waste 150

Constructing a pyramid of energy

Key points

- Energy pyramids are **always** a stepped pyramid shaped because energy is lost going from one trophic level up to the next.
- The lowest bar represents gross primary productivity or gross production.
- The width of the bars must be drawn to scale.
- The height of the bars is not significant but they should be uniform.
- The bars are centred.

Using the data from the forest ecosystem above.

Trophic Level	Energy / kJ m^{-2} year^{-1}
Producers	44000
Primary consumers	3000
Secondary consumers	700

Scale 1mm = 300 kJ m^{-2} year^{-1}

Secondary consumers

Primary consumers

Producers

IBHL Biology 2016 © Ashby Merson-Davies

Ecosystems
Key points
- ➤ An ecosystem is formed by the interaction between a community and its abiotic environment.
- ➤ An ecosystem has the potential to be sustainable over long periods of time if:
  - • sufficient sunlight falls on the ecosystem,
  - • the nutrients are recycled / replenished,
  - • the community is not damaged.
- ➤ Nutrients are obtained from the abiotic environment.
- ➤ The supply of nutrients is finite and limited.
- ➤ When organisms die and decompose the nutrients are returned to the environment.
- ➤ The nutrients can then be recycled.

Summary

Energy enters an ecosystem (usually) as light energy and leaves as heat energy.

Nutrients are recycled within the ecosystem.

Nutrients may leave one ecosystem, for example, by being washed or blown out, but they then usually enter another ecosystem – see blue box.

6.8 A pond ecosystem

6.9 A dust storm on the Bodélé Depression

Dust blown from a vast dried lake bed, the Bodélé Depression, in central Africa supplies essential nutrients to rainforest in the Amazon basin.

7. Name the trophic level of the organisms that start food chains.	8. What is the most common source of energy for ecosystems?	9. In what form is energy transferred within a food web?
10. List three ways energy is lost when passing through a trophic level.	11. State the approximate % efficiency of energy transfer through a trophic level.	12. In what form does energy leave an ecosystem?
	13. What is a population?	14. What is an abiotic environment?
15. What do you get when a community interacts with its abiotic environment?	16. What is meant by the term reproductive isolation?	

Carbon cycling

The carbon cycle
➢ Carbon cycles in two main forms, carbon dioxide and methane.
➢ Peat and fossil fuels link to the carbon dioxide cycle.
➢ These are shown separately as combining them would make the diagram too complex.
➢ The boxes with the brown outline link the three.
➢ The cycle starts with carbon dioxide in the atmosphere.

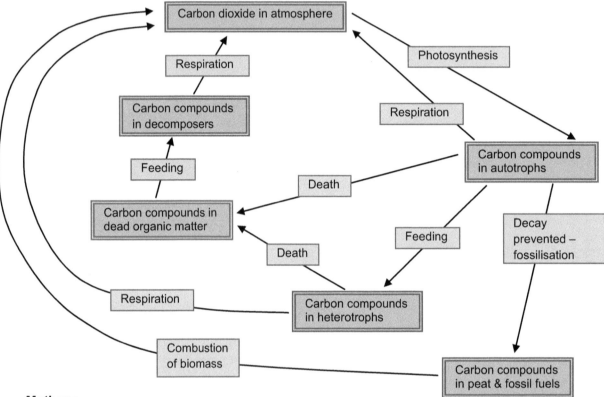

Methane
Key points
➢ In anaerobic conditions dead organic matter is converted to methane by methanogens.
➢ These are organisms belonging to the Domain Archaea.

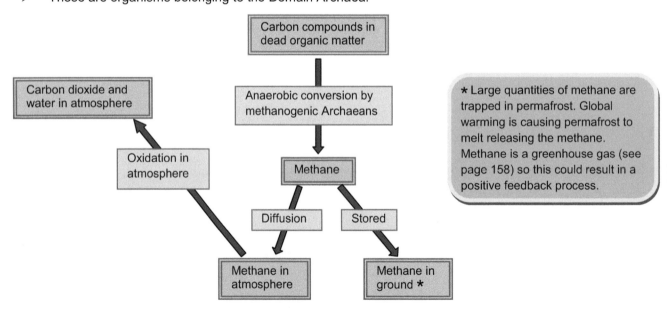

IBHL Biology 2016 © Ashby Merson-Davies

Peat, coal, oil and gas

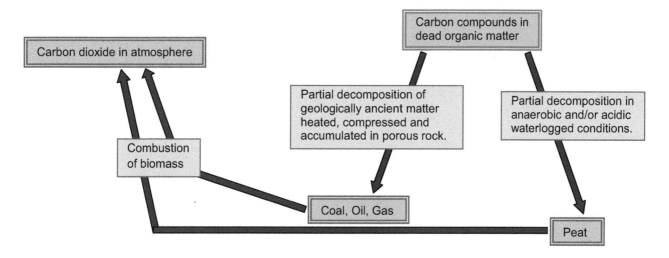

Large quantities of peat have been extracted from drained peat bogs and used as fuel or for gardening where it decomposes. In Indonesia large areas of dried peat are burning underground.

17. Name the process that converts atmospheric carbon dioxide to organic carbon compounds.	18. List two ways carbon dioxide is returned to the atmosphere in the carbon cycle.	19. Where do reef building corals obtain their carbon from?
20. Name the process by which organic compounds in autotrophs are transferred to heterotrophs.	21. In the carbon cycle what happens to biomass if decay is prevented?	22. What happens to carbon compounds in dead organisms?
23. What type of respiration do methanogenic bacteria use?	24. What does oxidation do to atmospheric methane?	25. Which Domain do methanogenic organisms belong to?

Climate change

The greenhouse effect

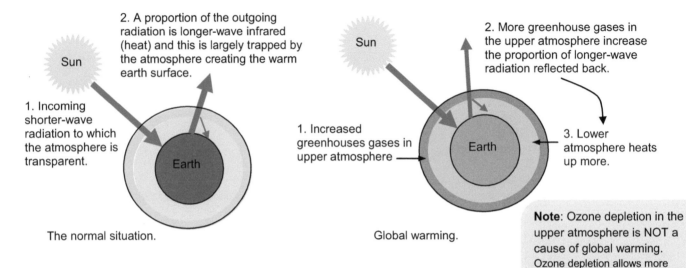

2. A proportion of the outgoing radiation is longer-wave infrared (heat) and this is largely trapped by the atmosphere creating the warm earth surface.

1. Incoming shorter-wave radiation to which the atmosphere is transparent.

The normal situation.

2. More greenhouse gases in the upper atmosphere increase the proportion of longer-wave radiation reflected back.

1. Increased greenhouses gases in upper atmosphere

3. Lower atmosphere heats up more.

Global warming.

Note: Ozone depletion in the upper atmosphere is NOT a cause of global warming. Ozone depletion allows more harmful UV radiation to reach the Earth's surface which increases the incidence of skin cancer.

Key points
➢ The greenhouse effect is a natural phenomenon and has helped to create a warm atmosphere that allowed evolution of life on the planet.
➢ The main greenhouse gases are carbon dioxide and water vapour.
➢ Other greenhouse gases which have less impact include methane and nitrogen oxides.
➢ The impact of a gas depends on:
  • its ability to absorb long wave radiation,
  • its concentration in the atmosphere.
➢ Carbon dioxide levels have been rising due to increasing use of fossil fuels in power stations, motor vehicles, aircraft and shipping.
➢ Aircraft also produce water vapour trails (contrails) which have an effect equal to their carbon dioxide emissions.
➢ Analysis of air bubbles trapped in Antarctica ice showed carbon dioxide levels remained fairly constant from 500BC to mid-1800s, the start of the industrial revolution.

6.10 Aircraft contrails

Date	Carbon dioxide concentration /ppm	% increase from 1880
1880	270	
1958	315	16.7
2000	360	33.3
2004	375	38.9
2006	382	41.5
2008	386	42.9
2010	390	44.4
2013	396	46.7

Table showing increase in atmospheric carbon dioxide since 1880

Data from the Mauna Loa monitoring station in Hawaii. (ppm = parts per million)

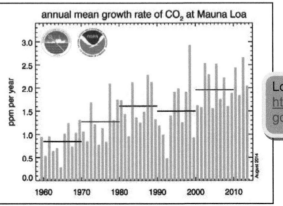

Look at this website
http://www.esrl.noa
gov/gmd/ccgg/trend

6.11 Graphs showing changes in atmospheric carbon dioxide since 1960 at Mauna Loa Observatory

IBHL Biology 2016 © Ashby Merson-Davies

- ➤ The gases in the upper atmosphere reflect back some of the heat rising from the Earth.
- ➤ This causes the atmosphere to heat up.
- ➤ Global temperatures and climate patterns are influenced by concentrations of greenhouse gases.
- ➤ This rising temperature can:
  - influence climate patterns:
    - increase frequency and severity of storms and hurricanes,
    - alter rainfall patterns causing droughts in some areas and flooding in others.
  - cause increased melting of glaciers, polar ice caps and sea ice leading to a rise in sea level,
  - cause a rise in sea levels due to thermal expansion of the oceans,
  - cause a rise in sea temperatures which leads to coral bleaching (death of coral),
  - increase evaporation so more atmospheric water vapour to increase greenhouse effect,
  - melt permafrost causing release of trapped methane,
  - enhance plant growth where plants have adequate water and minerals,
- ➤ Rising carbon dioxide levels increase acidity of the oceans causing weakening of coral reefs.

Human activities and climate change – evaluation

Activity and effect
- ➤ Burning fossil fuels to supply energy:
  - produces carbon dioxide and nitrogen oxides.
- ➤ Cutting down tropical rainforest:
  - reduces uptake of carbon dioxide due to photosynthesis,
  - increases carbon dioxide output from burning and rotting vegetation.
- ➤ Increase in cattle farming:
  - cattle produce methane.
- ➤ Increase in rice paddies:
  - anaerobic breakdown of organic compounds in the mud releases methane.
- ➤ Waste tips:
  - anaerobic breakdown of waste releases methane.

> A report from The Royal Institute of International Affairs in December 2014 stated that emissions from cattle equalled that of emissions from transport.

Key points
- ➤ Climate change is a better term than global warming because some regions of the globe will get colder as a result of increasing greenhouse gases.
- ➤ The graph below indicates that there is a close correlation between the rise in carbon dioxide concentration and the rise in global temperatures.

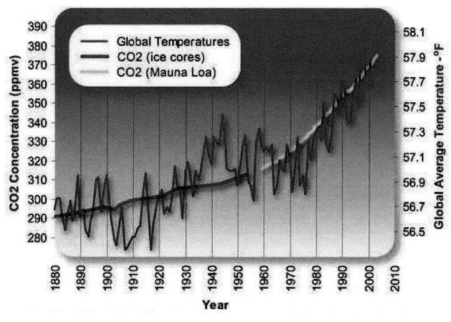

6.12 Graph showing the relationship between atmospheric carbon dioxide levels and global average temperature

American Secretary of State John Kerry said in a speech in Jakarta, Indonesia on 21st September 2014:
'In a sense, climate change can now be considered the world's largest weapon of mass destruction, perhaps even, the world's most fearsome weapon of mass destruction.'

Destruction of the rainforests

Accurate figures are difficult to obtain and it varies each year, but scientists generally agree that we are losing about 80,000 acres of tropical rainforest **daily**, and in addition significantly degrading a further 80,000 acres every day. Along with this plant loss go all the animals.

To put it another way a report in September 2014 stated that between 2000 and 2012 an area of rainforest equivalent to 5 football pitches was destroyed every **minute**. This is mostly driven by the demand for timber, leather, beef, soy and palm oil.

Healthy rainforest on the left and on the right cleared for palm oil plantations.

6.13 Rainforest destruction in Borneo

Coral reefs

Coral reefs are wonderfully diverse and productive ecosystems. They provide a vital resource for many coastal communities, provide breeding grounds for many fish species, and also protect the shoreline from the ocean waves.

Ocean acidification due to rising atmospheric carbon dioxide means corals are unable to absorb the calcium carbonate needed for their skeletons. Not only does this slow their growth but it weakens them making them more susceptible to wave damage. The oceans are now 30% more acidic than they were in 1750.

6.14 Reef damaged by waves. Fagatele Bay, American Samoa

Carbon fluxes

Key points

➤ Carbon flux is the flow of carbon from one carbon reservoir to another.
➤ There are four major carbon reservoirs:
  • atmosphere,
  • oceans,
  • Earth's crust,
  • terrestrial ecosystems.
➤ The net flux is the difference between input to the reservoirs and output from the reservoirs.
➤ The information above shows that the overall net flux is not only out of balance but getting worse.

<u>Diagram of carbon reservoirs and fluxes.</u>
Carbon stores in the coloured boxes are in gigatonnes, and the fluxes are in gigatonnes per year. (1 gigatonne = 1000,000,000,000kg)

© Kevin Saff at en.wikipedia [Public domain], from Wikimedia Commons.

"It is not so much that we are systematically annihilating life on this planet, but that there is nothing really being done about it, and worse still, nobody cares.

Indeed for governments throughout the world, the environment is little more than an embarrassment. Their main preoccupation is to earn the necessary foreign currency required to assure the economic development on which their prestige, power and future must depend. To this end they will sacrifice anything – their forests, their land, their topsoil, not to mention their traditions, their culture, their religion, indeed all that their ancestors, for countless generations, held to be most holy."

Edward Goldsmith, The retreat from Stockholm. *The Ecologist* (1982). p98. (Reprinted with permission).

26. What does plant matter that is partial decomposed in waterlogged anaerobic and/or acidic conditions become?	27. What happens to shorter wave radiation from the sun when it hits the Earth?	28. List the two main greenhouse gases.
29. List two additional greenhouse gases.	30. Why do greenhouse gases increase atmospheric temperatures?	31. List five effects of global warming.
32. What is a carbon reservoir?	33. List the four carbon reservoirs.	
34. What is meant by the term carbon flux?	35. What is meant by the term net carbon flux?	

Glossary

ABIOTIC	The non-living component of the environment.
DETRITUS	Non-living organic matter.
PPMV	Parts per million by volume.

Answers to Grey Box Questions

1a. First consumer. b. Second consumer. c. First consumer. d. Second consumer. e. Third consumer.
  f. Second consumer. g. Third consumer.
2. Heterotroph.   3. Detritivore.
4. Saprotroph.   5. First consumer.
6. Populations of different species living together and interacting with each other.
7. Producer / autotroph.   8. Sunlight.   9. Chemical.
10. Not consumed. Not assimilated. Respiration.   11. 10-20%
12. Heat.   13. A group of organisms of the same species living in the same place.
14. Non-living.   15. Ecosystem.
16. Members of a population that are unable to breed with a population of the same species due to some isolating factor, usually geographic.
17. Photosynthesis.   18. Respiration, burning, atmospheric oxidation of methane.
19. Dissolved carbon dioxide / hydrogen carbonate ions.   20. Feeding.
21. Peat and fossil fuels.   22. Consumed by decomposers.   23. Anaerobic.
24. Converts it to carbon dioxide and water.   25. Archaea.   26. Peat.
27. It becomes longer wave radiation.   28. Carbon dioxide. Water vapour.
29. Methane. Nitrogen oxides.   30. They reflect back to Earth more of the longer wave radiation.
31. Influence climate patterns / increase frequency and severity of storms and hurricanes / alter rainfall patterns causing droughts in some areas and flooding in others.
    Cause increased melting of glaciers, polar ice caps and sea ice leading to a rise in sea level.
    Cause a rise in sea levels due to thermal expansion of the oceans;
    Cause a rise in sea temperatures which leads to coral bleaching (death of coral).
    Increase evaporation so more water vapour to increase greenhouse effect;
    Melt permafrost causing release of trapped methane.
      Enhance plant growth where plants have adequate water and minerals.
32. A place where carbon is stored.
33. Atmosphere. Ocean. Earth's crust. Terrestrial ecosystems.
34. Movement of carbon between reservoirs.
35. The difference between input to reservoirs and the output from them.

IBHL Biology 2016 © Ashby Merson-Davies

Self-test Quiz

1. Food chains generally start with:
   a. herbivores,
   b. green plants,
   c. carnivores,
   d. decomposers.

2. In an ecosystem:
   a. energy is recycled,
   b. pyramids of energy always start with first consumers at the base,
   c. there are always three trophic levels,
   d. elements are recycled.

3. In an ecosystem which of the following is true?
   a. Respiration is part of the carbon cycle but photosynthesis is not.
   b. Green plants do not depend on decomposers.
   c. Green plants are affected by abiotic factors.
   d. Energy loss at each trophic level limits the number of trophic levels in a food chain to three.

4. A community can be defined as:
   a. a group of populations living with each other in an area,
   b. a group of organisms that can interbreed,
   c. the habitat in which the organisms are found,
   d. a group of populations living and interacting with the abiotic environment.

5. Which of the following statements is true?
   a. The trophic level of an organism is the height above ground where it is found.
   b. The transfer of energy from one trophic level to the next is never 100% efficient.
   c. There are always more carnivores in a food chain than herbivores.
   d. A food web always contains at least 10 organisms.

6. The initial source of energy for most communities is:
   a. light energy,
   b. chemical energy,
   c. green plants,
   d. producers.

7. Decomposers are:
   a. saprotrophic fungi and bacteria,
   b. producers,
   c. piles of dead plant and animal material,
   d. detritivores.

8. The greenhouse effect is due to:
   a. an increase in the amount of heat energy reflected from the earth's surface,
   b. an increase in the heat output of the sun,
   c. a decrease in the proportion of solar energy radiated back into space from the earth's atmosphere,
   d. an increase in heat output from the earth's surface due to the rise in human population.

9. A food web is:
   a. a complex food chain,
   b. food chains that include decomposers,
   c. all of the producers in a community,
   d. a group of interlinking food chains.

10. A pyramid of energy is always pyramid shaped because:
    a. there are always more consumers than producers,
    b. energy is lost between one trophic level and the next one up,
    c. most food chains start with light energy from the sun,
    d. carnivores consume more energy finding food than herbivores.

11. Look at the following food chain and select the correct statement.
    seeds → rat → cobra → mongoose
    a. The mongoose is a fourth consumer.
    b. The rat is a carnivorous consumer.
    c. The cobra is a second consumer.
    d. The rat is a producer.

12. Which of the following are greenhouse gases?
    a. water vapour , methane, carbon dioxide, nitrogen oxide,
    b. nitrogen oxide, carbon dioxide, hydrogen, oxygen,
    c. methane, carbon dioxide, nitrogen oxide, ozone,
    d. nitrogen oxide, water vapour, methane, ozone.

13. The efficiency of energy transfer within a food web:
    a. is determined by the length of the food chains,
    b. is about 50%,
    c. is determined by the efficiency of the producers,
    d. is about 10%.

14. An ecosystem is formed as a result of:
    a. an interaction between a population and its abiotic environment,
    b. an interaction between a community and its abiotic environment,
    c. an interaction between a population and a community,
    d. an interaction between different species.

15. Which of the following statements about the carbon cycle is correct?
    a. Carbon dioxide diffuses into water and can be used by aquatic autotrophs.
    b. Carbon dioxide is used by decomposers to make organic carbon compounds.
    c. Photosynthesis releases carbon dioxide which is used by plants to make organic compounds.
    d. Carbohydrates are converted to organic carbon compounds by respiration in decomposers.

16. Which of the following statements is correct?
    a. Methanogenic Archaea convert methane into carbon dioxide.
    b. Methanogenic Archaea convert carbon dioxide in the atmosphere into methane.
    c. Methane in the atmosphere can be oxidised into water and carbon dioxide.
    d. Water and carbon dioxide in the atmosphere can be oxidised into methane.

17. Which of the following is correct concerning global warming?
    a. It can adversely affect climate.
    b. It can lead to increased acidification of the oceans.
    c. It can cause increased melting of polar ice caps and sea ice.
    d. All of the above.

18. The net carbon flux can be described as:
    a. The change in the atmospheric carbon dioxide concentration.
    b. The difference between the flow of carbon into a reservoir and the flow of carbon out of it.
    c. The transfer of carbon to the atmospheric reservoir.
    d. The transfer of carbon from the ocean and Earth's crust reservoirs.

19. Increasing the dissolved carbon dioxide in the oceans can result in:
    a. damage to coral reefs due to the decrease in pH,
    b. an increase in the melting of the polar ice caps,
    c. an increase in the longer wavelength radiation from the sun radiated from the ocean surface,
    d. a reduction in the number of hydrogen carbonate ions available for marine Molluscs to use for shell building.

20. Look at the left graph (6.11) on page 158. The reason for the annual fluctuation is:
    a. Tropical rainforest trees lose their leaves in the winter.
    b. There is a greater uptake of carbon dioxide in the northern hemisphere forests in summer.
    c. Light intensity in the northern hemisphere fluctuates more than in the southern hemisphere.
    d. Temperatures in the tropics are higher than in higher latitudes.

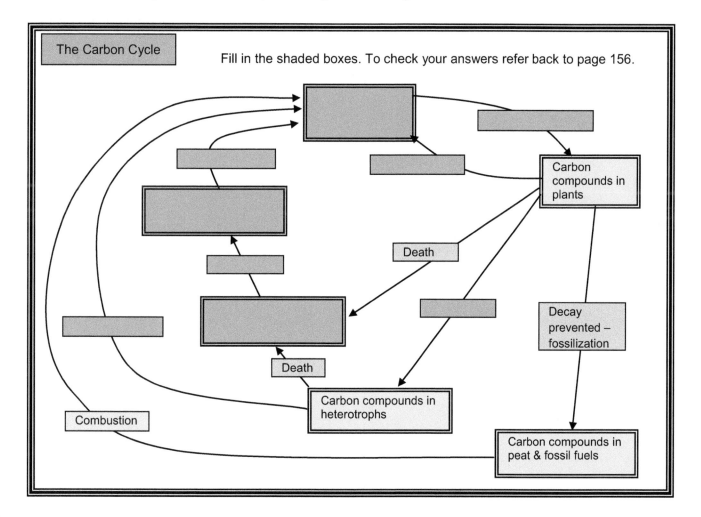

The Carbon Cycle

Fill in the shaded boxes. To check your answers refer back to page 156.

Carbon compounds in plants

Death

Decay prevented – fossilization

Death

Combustion

Carbon compounds in heterotrophs

Carbon compounds in peat & fossil fuels

Chapter Seven

Genetics

This is the story of heredity, how information is passed from parents to offspring. Experimental work on genetics was started in the nineteenth century, and Gregor Mendel is considered to be the founding father. He was the first person to make thorough, quantitative observations of the patterns of inheritance along with mechanisms to explain them. His work studying the garden pea led to the development of his two simple laws.

Chromosomes

Key points

➢ Prokaryotes have a single circular chromosome.

➢ Some prokaryotes have plasmids – small circular pieces of DNA in the cytoplasm – see page 58.

➢ Eukaryotes have linear chromosomes associated with histone proteins.

➢ The number of chromosomes is a characteristic of members of a species.

➢ Eukaryotic nuclei can be diploid or haploid.

- A diploid nucleus has pairs of chromosomes called homologous pairs.
  - Homologous chromosomes carry the same sequence of genes but not necessarily the same alleles of those genes.
- A haploid nucleus has one chromosome from each homologous pair.

➢ Some eukaryotes have a pair of chromosomes called sex chromosomes that determine gender.

➢ The chromosomes other than the sex chromosomes are called autosomes.

➢ Chromosomes can be arranged into a karyogram – see page 85.

> A human female has 44 autosomes + the sex chromosomes XX.
> A human male has 44 autosomes + the sex chromosomes XY.

Genes, alleles and mutations

Key points

➢ A gene is a heritable factor that consists of a length of DNA on a chromosome and influences a specific characteristic.

➢ A gene occupies a specific position on a chromosome called its locus.

➢ The different forms of a gene are called alleles.

➢ Alleles differ from one another by one or only a few bases.

➢ New alleles are formed by mutations.

➢ Mutations can be at the gene level, (see page 168) or at the chromosome level – see page 84.

➢ Meiosis mixes alleles to produce variety in sexual reproduction – see page 84.

➢ Genome is the whole of the genetic information of an organism.

➢ Genome size is the total length of DNA in an organism and includes all the non-coding sequences.

➢ The Human Genome Project determined the entire base sequence of all the human chromosomes.

> Gene – flower colour,
>
> Alleles – red colour, blue colour.

> **Genome**
>
> In prokaryotes it is all the information in the single circular chromosome plus any plasmids.
>
> In eukaryotic animals it is all the information in a haploid set of chromosomes plus mitochondrial DNA.
>
> In eukaryotic plants it is all the information in a haploid set of chromosomes plus mitochondrial DNA plus chloroplast DNA.

> **Human genome project**
>
> This was started in 1990 as an international collaboration to determine the entire base sequence of the human genome. The sequence of the 3 billion base pairs was completed in 2003. Work continues on mapping the location of specific genes and the positions and functions of other base sequences.
>
> **Outcomes**
>
> - Improved knowledge of how human genes function.
> - Improved diagnosis of genetic disease.
> - Increased potential for gene therapy.
> - Increased potential to design drugs to combat genetic malfunctions.

7.1 DNA sequencing

Sickle cell anaemia – a base substitution mutation

Key points
➢ Caused by a mutation in one of the two haemoglobin genes.
➢ An amino acid called glutamic acid has been replaced by one called valine.
➢ The triplet CTC has mutated to CAC.
➢ When the triplet is transcribed the normal mRNA codon GAG becomes GUG.
➢ GAG would be translated into glutamic acid but GUG is translated into valine.

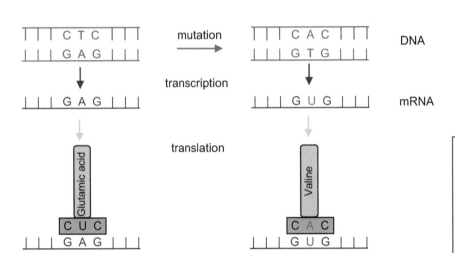

Hints:
- GAG has become GTG. **A** comes before **T** in the alphabet.
g for glutamic acid becomes **v** for valine and **g** comes before **v** in the alphabet.

Refer to the codon table on page 42 and look up the codons for these two amino acids.

If you **substitute** the A of the glutamic acid triplet with a U you will get a codon for valine.

Comparing diploid chromosome numbers of different species

Species	Diploid Number of Chromosomes
Parascaris equorum (parasitic worm)	2
Oryza sativa (rice)	24
Homo sapiens (human)	46
Pan troglodytes (chimpanzee)	48
Canis familiaris (domestic dog)	78

Human ancestors had the same number of chromosomes as chimpanzees – 48. By comparing chimp and modern human chromosomes it looks as though human chromosome 2 is a fusion of two smaller chimp chromosomes giving us 46.

Comparing chromosome and gene numbers of different species

Species	Number of Chromosomes	Estimated Number of Genes
Escherischia coli (bacterium)	One circular chromosome	1700 – 3000
Arabidopsis thaliana (plant)	10	23,000 – 25,000
Homo sapiens (human)	46	19,000 – 20,000
Drosophila melanogaster (fruit fly)	8	15,682
Mus musculus (House mouse)	40	25,000

Comparing genome size of different species

Species	Genome Size in Base Pairs
T2 bacteriophage (a bacterial virus)	0.17×10^6
Escherischia coli (bacterium)	4.6×10^6
Drosophila melanogaster (fruit fly)	130×10^6
Homo sapiens (human)	3200×10^6
Paris japonica (Japanese canopy plant)	$150,000 \times 10^6$

7.2 Flowers of *Paris japonica*.

Points of interest
➤ The number of chromosomes is highly variable between species.
➤ There is some correlation between size and number – the smaller the size the greater the number.
➤ The number of genes is highly variable between species.
➤ There is a positive correlation between genome size and complexity in prokaryotes.
➤ There is a positive correlation between genome size and complexity in eukaryotes but only in the more simple phyla.
➤ In the higher phyla there is much greater variability
➤ This is due to different proportions of non-coding DNA and repetitive sequences.
➤ Humans and most other mammals so far sequenced have roughly the same number of base pairs and genes.

Cairn's technique for measuring DNA molecules

Principles
➤ Thymidine is one of the four building blocks used in DNA replication – see page 40.
➤ It can be labelled with the radioactive form of hydrogen called tritium, ^3H.
➤ When tritium decays it emits a particle that marks a photographic plate.
➤ If cells are allowed to replicate in the presence of tritiated thymidine, $[^3H]$-T, the DNA becomes radioactive.

Key points
➤ Cairns used bacteria for his investigations.
➤ He cultured them with $[^3H]$-T.
➤ They were then treated with a hypotonic solution to lyse them (split them open).
➤ This would release the DNA.
➤ The solution was then spread on a photographic plate and left in the dark for many days to form an autoradiogram.
➤ After developing the film black dots could be seen where the bacterial chromosome had been.
➤ Since the experimental material was bacteria these dots formed circles.
➤ The circle could be measured to determine the length of the DNA molecule.

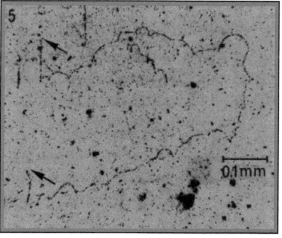

7.3 An autoradiogram of a Chinese hamster chromosome using Cairn's technique.
From arrow to arrow it is 1.6mm long. Exposure time was 3 months.

Radiation and gene mutation

Ionising radiation, X-rays, UV light and many chemicals are mutagens, i.e. they cause mutations. Scientists tracked the effects of ionising radiation after the Hiroshima and Nagasaki nuclear bombs, the nuclear power plant explosions at Chernobyl and Three Mile Island, and more recently at Fukushima due to the tsunami.

Hiroshima and Nagasaki
➤ Nuclear bombs were detonated over these Japanese cities in August 1945.
➤ Early in 1948 studies were begun to determine the after-effects of radiation using a city 29km south of Hiroshima as the control.
➤ It was found that birth defects were not significantly higher.
➤ However 200 cases of leukaemia (blood cancer) and 1700 cases of solid cancers could be attributed to radiation damage.

Chernobyl

- In April 1986 nuclear reactor No. 4 at Chernobyl exploded and caught fire.
- Several tons of radioactive material was released into the atmosphere, made worse by being carried up in the heat from the fire.
- 400× more radioactive material was released than from the Hiroshima bomb.
- This spread over huge areas of land, mainly Belarus, but including Ukraine, Russia, Germany, Scandinavian countries, southern Europe and the UK.
- Workers in the plant and rescue and firefighter person were either killed quickly or died within a few weeks from very high doses of radiation.
- Millions of people received increased doses of radiation.
- Mutations in new born farm animals in the fall-out area increased.
- Groundwater, and hence reservoirs, became contaminated as well as upland areas where contaminated rain fell.
- This led to food chain livestock – reindeer, sheep, cattle, wild boar – becoming contaminated with caesium-137.
- About 100,000km^2 of land was significantly contaminated.
- Thyroid cancer in children due to iodine-131 rose to over 6000 by 2005 with predictions of it rising very much higher.
- A report stated that there had been no increase in the rate of human birth defects or solid cancers.
- However it raised the possibility of long term genetic defects due to a large increase in mutations of non-coding DNA among children born in 1994.

Genetic modification and biotechnology

The polymerase chain reaction (PCR)
Key points
- This copies and amplifies minute quantities of DNA.
- Only specific parts of the DNA molecule are amplified.
- This is done by adding specific primers which bind to the complementary regions of DNA.
- The machine is automatically programmed to amplify the DNA.
- The DNA can then be used for profiling using gel electrophoresis.

7.4 A group of PCR machines.

The stages of the PCR

Gel electrophoresis
Key points
- The PCR is used to amplify the amount of DNA.
- The DNA is cut into fragments using restriction endonucleases.
- The fragments have a small negative charge.
- They will move through a gel towards a positive electrode.

> Restriction endonucleases are a group of enzymes obtained from bacteria that recognize very specific sequences of DNA and cut both of the DNA strands at this point.

> The smaller the fragment the further it will move.
> The DNA bands are stained.

wells

gel

positive electrode

bands of DNA fragments

7.5 The original autoradiograph, discovered by Professor Alec Jeffreys at Leicester University.

For a larger image go to
http://wellcomeimages.org/
Image number b0005956

The first DNA fingerprint. The first three lanes contain DNA from a woman, her mother and her father respectively. Lanes 4—11 contain DNA from assorted other species including mouse, baboon, lemur, cow, grey seal and tobacco (last lane). The DNA probe used in this experiment detected tandemly repeated short stretches of DNA called minisatellites whose length varies between individuals.

7.6 An example produced using school equipment.

DNA profiling

Principles

> Tandem repeats are short sequences of DNA repeated many times.
> They vary between individuals so much that the probability of two individuals being the same is zero, excluding identical twins.
> PCR may be used to increase the amount of DNA.
> Great care to prevent contamination is required as the PCR will also amplify contaminant DNA.
> DNA is cut up with restriction endonucleases.
> Gel electrophoresis separates the DNA fragments.
> The banding patterns are compared.

Uses

> Paternity – sometimes a woman is unsure who the father might be, or the man disputes being the father or wants to know if he is the father. DNA profiling from a mouth swab is used.
> Forensic investigations – often tiny samples of DNA can be found such as a drop of blood or saliva, a hair follicle, scrapings under a finger nail, and the DNA can be amplified using the PCR before profiling.
> Family relationships for immigrants.
> Determining if rare birds and other animals being sold as captive bred have actually been captive bred or been stolen from the wild.
> Comparing DNA from fossils with modern organisms.
> Determining the contents of manufactured foods, especially those containing meat.

An example of how DNA profiling has been used to determine paternity

Male A Male B Male C Child Mother

The black arrows correspond to the mother.
The red arrows show that the father of the child is male C.

Production of human insulin using gene transfer

Key requirements
➢ The insulin gene.
➢ A plasmid.
➢ A host bacterium (*E.coli*).
➢ Four enzymes - reverse transcriptase,
                - DNA polymerase,
                - a restriction endonuclease,
                - DNA ligase.

> When genes are transferred between species the amino acid sequence of polypeptides translated from them is unchanged because the genetic code is universal.

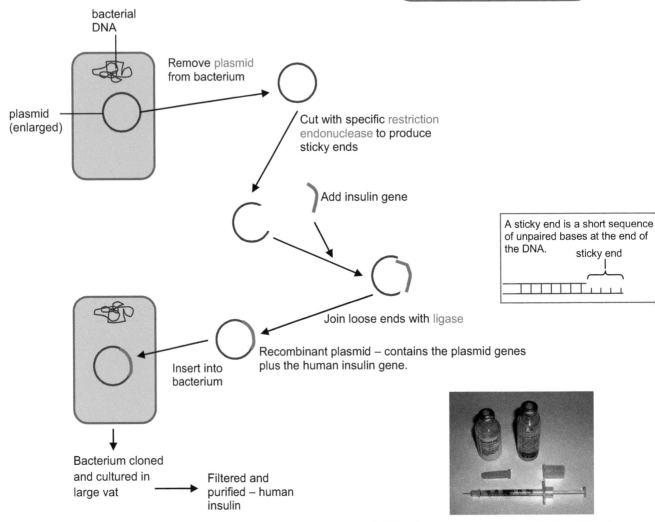

bacterial DNA

plasmid (enlarged)

Remove plasmid from bacterium

Cut with specific restriction endonuclease to produce sticky ends

Add insulin gene

> A sticky end is a short sequence of unpaired bases at the end of the DNA.
>
> sticky end

Join loose ends with ligase

Recombinant plasmid – contains the plasmid genes plus the human insulin gene.

Insert into bacterium

Bacterium cloned and cultured in large vat → Filtered and purified – human insulin

7.7 Insulin syringes are marked in 'insulin' units.

The insulin gene
Key points
➢ The gene cannot be cut from the beta cell DNA because it will produce primary RNA which contains introns.

➢ Insulin mRNA from the cytoplasm is obtained.

➢ The enzymes reverse transcriptase and DNA polymerase are used to make a DNA molecule from the mRNA.

➢ A specific sequence of bases is added at each end and then cut with the same restriction endonuclease as used on the plasmid to make the same sticky ends.

> Introns are short sequences of bases that are cut from the primary RNA to leave mRNA.

Genetically modified organisms (GMOs)

Key points

➤ Since the genetic code is (nearly) universal genetic information can be transferred between organisms.

➤ New varieties can be produced much more quickly than through conventional breeding.

➤ Novel genes can be introduced which are not in the species' genome.

➤ It does raise questions of ethics and safety.

Examples currently in commercial use

Soybean	Tolerance to the herbicide glyphosate by inserting a gene from a soil bacterium.
Corn	Resistance to insect pests, specifically the corn borer, by inserting a gene from a bacterium which produces a toxic protein.
Altered fatty acid composition in canola beans	High laurate levels achieved by inserting a gene from the California bay tree. (Laurate is used in soap manufacture.)
Virus resistance in plum	Resistance to plum pox virus conferred by inserting a coat protein gene from the virus.

Examples in development

Golden rice	Modified using three genes to produce high levels of beta-carotene, a precursor for vitamin A.
Vaccines	Tobacco engineered to produce hepatitis B antigen for vaccine production.
Oral vaccine for chickens	Corn engineered to produce a protein from the Newcastle disease virus in its seeds induced an immune response in chickens when fed to them.

Benefits of GM

Corn
The added gene comes from the bacterium *Bacillus thuringiensis* so the GM variety is called Bt corn. Caterpillars eating any part of the plant will be killed by the bacterial toxin.
Benefit – the toxin is specific to pests eating the plant and does not harm other animals. The crop does not have to be sprayed with insecticides which would kill beneficial insects. This also reduces costs associated with manufacture and application of the insecticide.

Soybean
Glyphosate is a biodegradable general herbicide. The soybean crop is allowed to germinate and then sprayed once with glyphosate. The weeds are killed and then continued growth of the soybean out-competes any new weeds that germinate.
Benefit – reduced competition for soil nutrients increases crop yield.

Bt Corn
The toxin is expressed in all parts of the plant including the pollen. The plant is wind pollinated so the pollen blows around and lands on the leaves of other plants leading to concerns that it could kill insects feeding on those leaves. Research was done with larvae of the Monarch butterfly that feeds on milkweed. Laboratory tests showed that the larvae were indeed harmed when Bt corn pollen was sprinkled on the milkweed leaves. However the tests were shown to have used amounts of pollen that would not be encountered in the field and Bt corn was licenced for continued use.

Canola
Canola is a variety of rape which is normally low in laurate. Laurate for soap making has been obtained from coconut, palm and laurel oils.
Benefit – GM canola can be grown easily and cheaply and in large quantities. Palm oil plantations have resulted in vast areas of tropical rainforest being destroyed, so using GM canola can reduce this destruction.

Newcastle disease
This is a highly contagious and virulent virus and is found worldwide. Chickens are an important food source for both eggs and low fat meat.
Potential benefit – Immunising both small and large flocks would be simple and productivity would be greatly increased.

Risks of GM

➢ See Bt corn above.
➢ Widespread use of pest resistant crop plants may result in the pests developing resistance to the toxin, though this frequently happens with other forms of pest control.
➢ There are concerns that the proteins from transgenic genes could be toxic or cause allergic reactions in livestock or humans if they would not normally have encountered them.
➢ During the procedure to transfer genes into bacteria antibiotic resistance genes are used to test whether the desired gene has been transferred. These antibiotic resistance genes would be dangerous if they spread to pathogenic bacteria.
➢ Transferred genes could mutate and create problems. During the risk assessment for the transfer mutations would be difficult to predict and could not therefore be included in the assessment.
➢ Transferred genes in plants could spread to other species through cross pollination. These plants could then become toxic to wildlife or become uncontrollable weeds.
➢ Herbicide resistant plants could grow the following year from spilled seed. These would be a nuisance if the new crop was different as they could not be controlled.

Nature, January 2015 – GM microbes created that can't escape the lab
Genetically engineered micro-organisms are used in Europe, the US and China to produce drugs under controlled industrial conditions. Preventing these micro-organisms from escaping into the environment – biocontainment – has been an important area of research. Two laboratories in the US have recoded the *E. coli* bacteria genome so that they require a synthetic amino acid in order to make an essential protein. Without this amino acid they cannot make the protein and without the protein they die. Work is continuing to increase the number of synthetic amino acids required.

Cloning

Key points

➢ A clone is a group of cells or organisms that are genetically identical because they have come from a single parent.
➢ Many plant species and some animal species have natural methods of cloning.
➢ Horticulturists can increase the numbers of a new plant variety or of an endangered plant by taking cuttings or micropropagation.
➢ Cloning can be done with animals after IVF. When the zygote divides the cells can be separated and each will develop into an embryo.
➢ This can be done several times to produce a number of embryos.

This can happen naturally resulting in identical twins.

These are the stems from the parent plant.

Buds grow into new plants which put down roots and can eventually break off from the parent.

7.8 Strawberry runners

7.9 A cluster of greenfly on a rose. Female greenfly give birth to live young without fertilisation, a process called parthenogenesis.

Somatic cell nuclear transfer (SCNT)

Key points

- ➤ This is a technique for cloning an adult animal.
- ➤ The first steps were done by John Gurdon on amphibians.
- ➤ He removed nuclei from body cells of Xenopus tadpoles and transplanted them into enucleated egg cells.
- ➤ The egg cells behaved as though they were zygotes and developed into mature frogs.
- ➤ It was first done in a mammal by Dr Ian Wilmut who created Dolly the sheep in 1996.

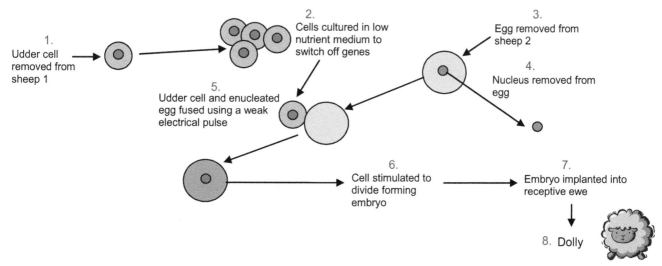

- ➤ To date human SCNT has met with very limited success partly due to very strict regulations and the failure to find the right protocol to stimulate development.
- ➤ Creating an embryo from a patient would mean being able to harvest pluripotent embryonic stem cells which could be used to treat the patient – refer back to pages 55 and 86.
- ➤ However techniques were developed in 2006 to induce adult cells to become pluripotent stem cells, negating the need for SCNT.

Theoretical genetics
Key vocabulary

> The definitions are critical and really must be learnt or you will not be able to understand genetics problems or write good answers.

Gene	A heritable factor that controls a specific characteristic.
Allele	A specific form of a gene, occupying the same gene locus as other alleles of that gene, but differing from other alleles by small differences in its base sequence.
Dominant allele	An allele that has the same effect on the phenotype when in either the homozygous or heterozygous state.
Recessive allele	An allele that only has an effect on the phenotype when it is in the homozygous state.
Genotype	The alleles possessed by an organism.
Phenotype	The characteristics of an organism.
Heterozygous	Having two different alleles at a gene locus.
Homozygous	Having two identical alleles at a gene locus.
Codominant	Pairs of alleles that both affect the phenotype when present in the heterozygous state.
Locus	The specific position on a homologous chromosome of a gene. (Plural loci).
Carrier.	An individual that has a recessive allele of a gene that causes an adverse effect when homozygous.
Sex linkage	The pattern of inheritance characteristic of genes located on the sex chromosomes.
Test cross	Testing a phenotypically dominant phenotype to determine if it is heterozygous or homozygous.
Pure or true breeding	A parent where the dominant phenotype is homozygous.
F_1	First filial generation, i.e. offspring from the parental generation.
F_2	Second filial generation only obtained by crossing F_1 with F_1.

Inheritance

> Mendel discovered the principles of inheritance using the garden pea and established his two Laws.

Mendel and inheritance

Gregor Mendel was a monk in a monastery in Brno in what is now the Czech Republic. He approached the problem of inheritance from a mathematical point of view and used the common garden pea to obtain the large numbers he needed. The pea also had the advantage that there were a number of distinct varieties of flower colour, seed colour and shape, and plant height. This meant he could carry out many cross breeding experiments in order to find patterns and deduce the principles of inheritance. Mendel did not know about chromosomes or genes – he used the term 'factors' which we know call genes. Although he published his work in 1865/6 it was not well known and dismissed or ignored by other biologists. The principles of genetics were 'discovered' again in 1900 but the researchers then found Mendel's publication and realised he had discovered the principles 35 years earlier.

7.10 The garden pea

Key principles

> Most gamete producing cells are diploid.
> Therefore alleles are in pairs.
> Gametes are produced by meiosis.
> Therefore gametes are haploid and contain only one allele from a pair.
> Fusion of haploid gametes to form the zygote restores the diploid number.
> Random fertilisation mixes alleles.

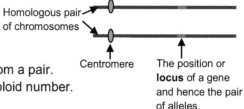

Homologous pair of chromosomes

Centromere

The position or **locus** of a gene and hence the pair of alleles.

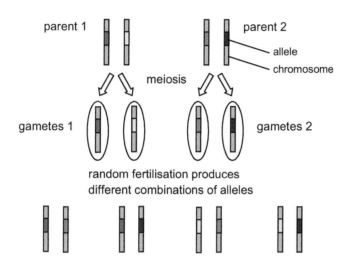

parent 1

parent 2

allele

chromosome

meiosis

gametes 1

gametes 2

random fertilisation produces different combinations of alleles

Genetics problems

Key points for answering genetics problems

> **ALWAYS** choose a letter to represent a gene where the upper and lower case are distinct. When you are quickly writing out a problem you could easily get them muddled when you have separated them into gametes.
> Always set out a genetics answer fully and clearly showing:

- ◆ key
- ◆ the parental phenotype
- ◆ the parental genotype
- ◆ the gametes in circles
- ◆ the first filial generation

and if required

- ◆ the second gametes, G_2
- ◆ the second filial generation, F_2.

> A phenotype is expressed in words.
> A genotype is expressed in letters.

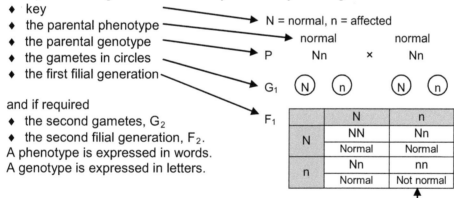

N = normal, n = affected

		N	n
N		NN	Nn
		Normal	Normal
n		Nn	nn
		Normal	Not normal

This is called a **Punnett grid.** Note that it includes both genotypes and phenotypes.

Key points for solving genetics problems

> Genetics problems are easy if you know the clues to look for.
> All problems you will be asked to solve fall into four types:
>   1. Monohybrid.
>   2. Codominance.
>   3. Multiple alleles.
>   4. Sex linkage.

One worked example is given for each type of cross and then there is a second problem for you to try. The answer is at the end of the Chapter.

Genetic disorders in humans

➢ Many have been identified but most are rare.
➢ Most are on the autosomes but some are sex linked.

Disorder	Chromosome	Dominant or recessive
Huntingdon's	4	Dominant
Haemophilia	X	Recessive
Colour blindness	X	Recessive
Cystic fibrosis	7	Recessive
Duchenne muscular dystrophy	X	Recessive
Phenylketonuria	12	Recessive
Sickle cell	11	Codominant
Tay-Sachs	15	Recessive

Some human genetic disorders. You need to know the coloured boxes.

The test cross

Key points

➢ This is done in order to determine whether a dominant phenotype is homozygous or heterozygous.
➢ This is **always** crossed with the homozygous recessive.
➢ If the dominant phenotype is heterozygous we would expect 50% of the offspring to show the recessive phenotype.

P   Long winged   x   Short wing
                 Ll   ll

G   Ⓛ   Ⓘ   Ⓘ

F₁

		l
	L	Ll
		50% long winged
	l	ll
		50% short winged

Each box contains a definition. State the word being defined. **Check your answers on page 176.**	1. An allele that has the same effect on the phenotype when in either the homozygous or heterozygous state.	2. A specific form of a gene, occupying the same gene locus as other alleles of that gene.
3. The alleles possessed by an organism.	4. The specific position on a homologous chromosome of a gene.	5. Having two different alleles at a gene locus.
6. A heritable factor that controls a specific characteristic.	7. The characteristics of an organism.	8. An allele that only has an effect on the phenotype when it is in the homozygous state.
9. The pattern of inheritance characteristic of genes located on the sex chromosomes.	10. Testing a phenotypically dominant phenotype to determine if it is heterozygous or homozygous.	11. A parent where the dominant phenotype is homozygous.
12. An individual that has a recessive allele of a gene that causes an adverse effect when homozygous.	13. Having two identical alleles at a gene locus.	14. Pairs of alleles that both affect the phenotype when present in the heterozygous state.

Monohybrid crosses

- This is the basic cross. Make sure you master this before going further.

PROBLEM
Pure breeding long winged flies are crossed with short winged flies and all the offspring are long winged. Long wings is dominant. When these offspring are crossed with short winged flies approximately one half of the offspring have short wings. Explain fully.

SOLUTION.
We are told long wings is dominant so we can choose letters.
We are also told the long winged flies are pure breeding which means the genotype is homozygous. The genotype must be LL. The short wing parents must be ll as l is recessive.

Key L = long, l = short.

Parental phenotype   Long wing   x   Short wing
Parental genotype   LL   ll

G

F$_1$ Ll
                     All long winged

There are only two types of gamete so we do not need a Punnett grid.

Notice that on the gametes row we only need to write one L and one l. This is because all the gametes from each parent are the same and so there is no need to write more. This saves time in the exam.

Now for the second part of the problem. Since we are not crossing offspring amongst themselves we have to start with P again.

Parental phenotype   Long winged offspring   x   Short wing
Parental genotype   Ll   ll

G   L   l   l

F$_1$

	l
L	Ll 50% long winged
l	ll 50% short winged

Since there are more than two types of gamete we need a Punnett grid.

In theory we get a 50:50 or 1:1 ratio. In the actual cross we get approximately 50:50 and so, allowing for random fertilisation, our actual or observed ratio fits our ratio predicted from the Punnett grid above.

PROBLEM 1

The Under Dog normally has very short legs but there is also a recessive mutation that has long legs. A Dog homozygous for short legs was crossed with one with long legs. The F$_1$ puppies were crossed with Dogs that were heterozygous for short legs. Predict the outcome of these F$_1$ crosses.

Answer page 184.

Codominance

- Codominance simply means that **both** alleles have an effect on the phenotype.
- Do NOT describe them as both being dominant.
- The alleles are shown in a different way from a monohybrid cross. A capital letter is used for the gene with a capital suffix for the allele.

> **Recognition feature:**
> There are three phenotypes, the third one being a blend/mixture of the other two.

PROBLEM

A mouse with white fur was crossed with one with black fur and all the offspring have grey fur. Show this cross in a genetics diagram and deduce the phenotypes and phenotype ratio of the F_2 generation.

SOLUTION.

There are three phenotypes so this clearly indicates codominance, the grey being a blend of white and black. This means that both the white and the black parents have to be homozygous. To choose the symbol we can use F for fur and W and B for the colours.

Key F^W = white, F^B = black.

P   White fur   x   Black fur
          $F^W F^W$ $F^B F^B$

G_1 F^W F^B

F_1 $F^W F^B$
          All grey fur

> 'Parent phenotype' and 'Parent genotype' have been simplified to 'P'.

Second cross

     Grey fur   x   Grey fur
       $F^W F^B$ $F^W F^B$

> This is a cross of F_1 x F_1 and so the offspring are F_2.

G_2 F^W F^B F^W F^B

F_2

	F^W	F^B
F^W	$F^W F^W$	$F^W F^B$
	white	grey
F^B	$F^W F^B$	$F^B F^B$
	grey	black

> Adding the phenotypes to the table makes it easier to count the ratio.

The F_2 ratio is 1 white : 2 grey : 1 black.

PROBLEM 2

The cannabis plant, Cannibis sativa, produces two chemicals, THC and CBD, controlled by a pair of codominant alleles. A heterozygous plant produces both chemicals in equal quantities. Two heterozygous plants were crossed and 460 seeds collected. When these were grown approximately 230 of the plants produced THC and CBD in equal amounts. Deduce the approximate numbers of plants that produced only THC and only CBD.

Answer page 185.

Multiple alleles

- Usually within a population there are many alleles of a gene and this is logically called multiple alleles.
- However any one individual can only have two of these alleles because it has only one pair of loci for any given gene.
- The example you have to know is the ABO blood grouping.
- There are three alleles – I^A, I^B, and i.
- This is an unusual case though because they also show codominance – alleles I^A and I^B are codominant.
- This results in four different phenotypes or blood groups.

Genotypes	Phenotype or blood group
I^AI^A or I^Ai	A
I^BI^B or I^Bi	B
I^AI^B	AB
ii	O

PROBLEM

Claire is blood group A and her husband Clive is blood group O. Celine is blood group AB and her husband David is blood group B. At the hospital Claire and Celine's baby girls were born at the same time but Claire feels the staff accidentally muddled them up. Baby Melissa given to Celine is blood group O. Explain how this could solve the difficulty.

SOLUTION

If the baby is blood group O it's genotype must be ii. Celine is blood group AB and therefore has the genotype I^AI^B so she cannot give an i allele to the baby. Claire is blood group A and so either has the genotype I^AI^A or I^Ai. Clive has to have the genotype ii. This means that baby Melissa must belong to Claire and Clive.

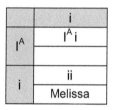

P — Claire I^Ai — Clive ii — Celine I^AI^B — David I^Bi

We will assume David is I^Bi although he could be I^BI^B.

G — I^A i i — I^A I^B I^B i

F₁

	i
I^A	I^Ai
i	ii Melissa

	I^B	i
I^A	I^AI^B Group AB	I^Ai Group A
I^B	I^BI^B Group B	I^Bi Group B

None of these genotypes is ii and so cannot be Melissa even if David is I^Bi.

PROBLEM 3

Sufyan is blood group A and Chiara is group B. Their first baby is group O and their second group AB. Explain how this is possible.

Answer page 185.

Sex linkage

- In humans (and some other organisms) two chromosomes, the sex chromosomes, determine gender.
- All the other chromosomes are called autosomes.
- The female sex chromosomes are XX and the male sex chromosomes are XY.
- Sex linked genes are only found on the X chromosome and not on the shorter Y chromosome.

X
Y

This region of the X chromosome carries the sex linked genes.

- Only females can be heterozygous or homozygous with respect to sex linked genes.
- Individuals have two phenotypes – the characteristic on the X chromosome **and** the gender.
- Males produce X sperm and Y sperm and therefore determine the gender of the offspring.
- A female carrier must be heterozygous as one X chromosome has the dominant allele and the other has the recessive allele. $X^A X^a$.
- The sex ratio in the offspring is always 1:1.

The commonest mistake with sex linkage problems is that students forget that the Y chromosome does <u>not</u> carry an allele.

A simple way of avoiding this mistake is to write the symbol Y^-.

Writing − next to the Y will prevent you from putting an allele there.

You need to know:
Colour-blindness and haemophilia are examples of sex linked characteristics.
Both are recessive.

PROBLEM
Ethan had haemophilia but Sasha, his wife, was normal and not a carrier. Their daughter Karen married Jacob who also had haemophilia. Determine the phenotypes of their sons and daughters.

SOLUTION
Ethan must have had the genotype $X^h Y^-$ since he had haemophilia. Karen inherited his X^h chromosome, but her other X chromosome from her mother was normal X^H. Thus Karen had the genotype $X^H X^h$ so she was a carrier. Jacob had to be $X^h Y^-$ as he had haemophilia.

Key H = the normal allele, h = the haemophilia allele.

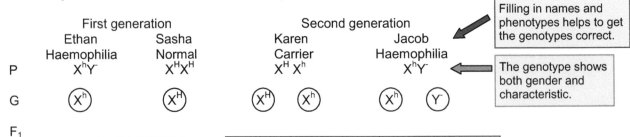

First generation		Second generation	
Ethan	Sasha	Karen	Jacob
Haemophilia	Normal	Carrier	Haemophilia
$X^h Y^-$	$X^H X^H$	$X^H X^h$	$X^h Y^-$

P

G X^h X^H X^H X^h X^h Y^-

Filling in names and phenotypes helps to get the genotypes correct.

The genotype shows both gender and characteristic.

F₁

	X^H
X^h	$X^H X^h$
	Karen

	X^h	Y^-
X^H	$X^H X^h$	$X^H Y^-$
	Female, carrier	Male, normal
X^h	$X^h X^h$	$X^h Y^-$
	Female with haemophilia	Male with haemophilia

PROBLEM 4

A man with normal colour vision married a woman who also had normal colour vision. However two of their five children were colour blind. Explain how this could have arisen, showing which children they were.

Answer page 186.

Pedigree charts

- This is another way of showing genetic crosses but for several generations.
- Gametes are not shown.
- There are standard symbols.

Normal female   Normal male   Affected female   Affected male

Heterozygotes may be shown as ⊙ ⊡

The symbol for a heterozygous individual is rather variable. Sometimes half the square or circle is filled in, sometimes there is a black dot in the middle of the square or circle. The question will have a key, or if **you** draw it **you** have to provide a key.

Example

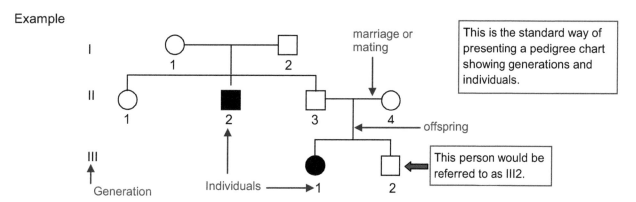

marriage or mating

This is the standard way of presenting a pedigree chart showing generations and individuals.

offspring

This person would be referred to as III2.

Some information has deliberately been missed from the above diagram but we can deduce it.
Two common questions are – 1. Is the disorder dominant or recessive? 2. Is the disorder sex linked?

The disorder has to be recessive since neither individual in generation I has it but II2 does have it. Similarly III1 has it but neither of her parents.

Is it sex linked? Remember that sex linked alleles are only on the X chromosome. If we give the symbol n to the disorder then III1 must be $X^n X^n$. One X^n must have come from her father making him $X^n Y$. He should show the disorder but he doesn't, and thus from this we can deduce that the gene is not sex linked. A useful hint is that it is often a male that provides the essential clue.
We can now continue to deduce that both I1 and I2 must be heterozygous, and also II3 and II4.
We could now show this in a Punnett grid. Use N for the dominant normal allele and n for the recessive disorder allele.

Parent I2

	N	n
N	NN	Nn
n	Nn	nn

Parent I1

Individual II3

PROBLEM 5

The pedigree chart below shows the inheritance of hairy ears in rabbits. An open symbol is hairy and a black symbol is smooth. Deduce whether smooth ears is dominant or recessive.

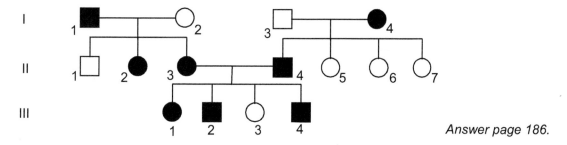

Answer page 186.

Solutions to Chapter Problems

Problem 1

The Under Dog normally has very short legs but there is also a recessive mutation that has long legs. A Dog homozygous for short legs was crossed with one with long legs. The F₁ puppies were crossed with Dogs that were heterozygous for short legs. Predict the outcome of these F₁ crosses.

Solution
We are told the short leg dog is homozygous, and the dog with long legs also has to be homozygous because long is recessive.

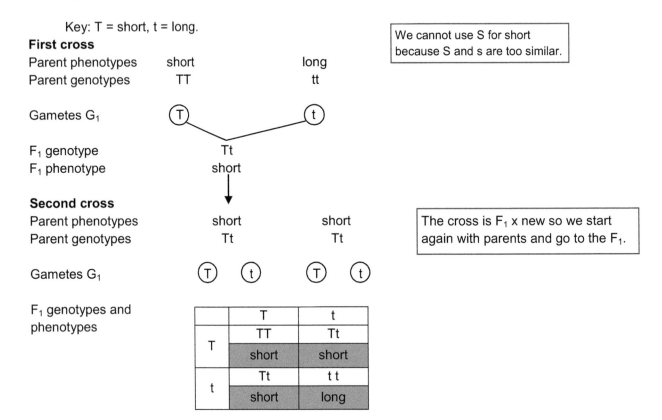

| | | Key: T = short, t = long. | | We cannot use S for short because S and s are too similar. |

First cross

| Parent phenotypes | short | long |
| Parent genotypes | TT | tt |

Gametes G₁   (T)   (t)

F₁ genotype — Tt
F₁ phenotype — short

Second cross

| Parent phenotypes | short | short |
| Parent genotypes | Tt | Tt |

The cross is F₁ x new so we start again with parents and go to the F₁.

Gametes G₁   (T) (t)   (T) (t)

F₁ genotypes and phenotypes

	T	t
T	TT short	Tt short
t	Tt short	t t long

For the first cross all the F₁ Under Dogs will be heterozygous and therefore have short legs. In the second cross though there will be a ratio of three Dogs with short legs to one Dog with long legs. One third of the Dogs with short legs will have a homozygous genotype and two thirds will have a heterozygous genotype.

IBSL Biology 2016 © Ashby Merson-Davies

PROBLEM 2

The cannabis plant, Cannibis sativa, produces two chemicals, THC and CBD, controlled by a pair of codominant alleles. A heterozygous plant produces both chemicals in equal quantities. Two heterozygous plants were crossed and 460 seeds collected. When these were grown approximately 230 of the plants produced THC and CBD in equal amounts. Deduce the approximate numbers of plants that produced only THC and only CBD.

SOLUTION

Key C^T = THC plants; C^C = CBD plants

| Parent phenotypes | THC/CBD | THC/CBD |
| Parent genotypes | $C^T C^C$ | $C^T C^C$ |

Gametes G_1 : C^T C^C C^T C^C

F$_1$ genotypes and phenotypes

		C^T	C^C
C^T		$C^T C^T$	$C^T C^C$
		THC	THC/CBD
C^C		$C^T C^C$	$C^C C^C$
		THC/CBD	CBD

The ratio is 1THC : 2THC/CBD : 1CBD. 25% or approximately 115 plants will only produce THC, and the same for plants only producing CBD.

PROBLEM 3

Sufyan is blood group A and Chiara is group B. Their first baby is group O and their second group AB. Explain how this is possible.

SOLUTION

Since their first baby is group O it must have the genotype ii, and therefore both Sufyan and Chiara must have an i in their genotype. Sufyan is group A and therefore must have an I^A allele as well, so his genotype is $I^A i$. Similarly Chiara must have the genotype $I^B i$.

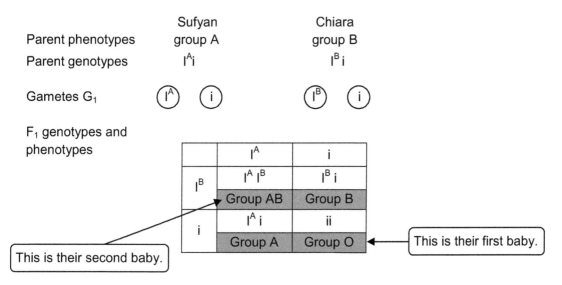

	Sufyan	Chiara
Parent phenotypes	group A	group B
Parent genotypes	$I^A i$	$I^B i$

Gametes G_1 : I^A i I^B i

F$_1$ genotypes and phenotypes

		I^A	i
I^B		$I^A I^B$	$I^B i$
		Group AB	Group B
i		$I^A i$	ii
		Group A	Group O

This is their second baby.

This is their first baby.

PROBLEM 4

A man with normal colour vision married a woman who also had normal colour vision. However two of their five children were colour blind. Explain how this could have arisen, showing which children they were.

SOLUTION

The only possibility here is for the woman to be a carrier. She will then pass a recessive colour blind allele to half of her sons. Since the man has normal vision none of their daughters can be colour blind though half of them will be carriers.

Key: N = normal vision, n = colour blindness.

	woman, carrier	man, normal
Parent phenotypes	woman, carrier	man, normal
Parent genotypes	$X^N X^n$	$X^N Y^-$

Gametes G_1 X^N X^n X^N Y

F$_1$ genotypes and phenotypes

		X^N	X^n
	X^N	$X^N X^N$	$X^N X^n$
		daughter normal	daughter, carrier
	Y^-	$X^N Y^-$	$X^n Y^-$
		son, normal	son, colour blind

PROBLEM 5

The pedigree chart below shows the inheritance of hairy ears in rabbits. An open symbol is hairy and a black symbol is smooth. Deduce whether smooth ears is dominant or recessive.

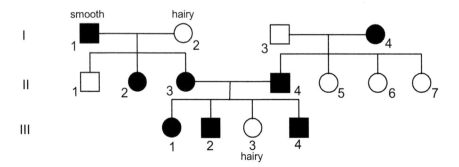

SOLUTION

There is nothing in either generation I or II to help as the pedigree will work with smooth ears being either dominant or recessive. The answer lies with generation III. If the smooth ear allele is recessive then II3 and II4 are both homozygous recessive. Therefore they could not have had III3 since this has hairy ears and must have at least one dominant allele. The smooth ear allele is therefore dominant. We can check this by working backwards. Then II3 and II4 are heterozygous. I1 and I4 must also be heterozygous.

IBSL Biology 2016 © Ashby Merson-Davies

Glossary

Contagious	Easily spread by contact.
Enucleated	A cell that has had its nucleus removed.
Genome size	The total number of DNA base pairs in one copy of a haploid genome.
Mutation	A spontaneous permanent change in the base sequence of DNA.
Non-coding sequences	Lengths of DNA that do not code for an RNA molecule, i.e. are not transcribed.
Primary RNA	This is the RNA strand produced by transcription of a gene in eukaryotes. It contains sequences of bases, called introns, which have to be removed. The remaining pieces of RNA are joined together to form mRNA which is translated.
Virulent	Violent.

Test Problems

Many of the organisms used here are imaginary to make a change from all the ones on mice, rabbits and fruit flies. Treat the genetics in the normal way though. The answers are in Appendix 2 on page 214.

1. Two black female mice were crossed with a grey male. In several litters female A produced 19 black and 18 grey young. Female B produced 25 black young.
   What can you deduce about the nature of black and grey fur colour in mice, and what are the genotypes of the parents?

2. Two yellow Bandycoots were thought by their keeper to be homozygous for coat colour. When they were mated all the babies were yellow. However when these offspring were later mated amongst themselves. The F_2 generation, some of these offspring were orange. This meant that one of the grandparents was heterozygous.
   How would you find out which grandparent was heterozygous?

3. In the Giant Boring beetle (*Coleopsis yawnii*) green eyes are dominant over blue. A blue-eyed beetle, both of whose parents had green eyes, was mated with a green-eyed beetle. They have one baby beetle which is blue-eyed. Deduce the genotypes of all these five individuals? If they have another baby beetle could it be green-eyed, and if so determine its genotype.

4. Once upon a time a Quoll with luminous eyes met a Quoll with blue eyes. Shortly afterwards several little Quolls were born and they all had luminous eyes. Deduce the genotypes of the parents and the offspring.
   Later on in life the little Quolls grew up and all but one met luminous eyed Quolls. All their babies had luminous eyes. The one lonely Quoll however met a beautiful blue-eyed Quoll and some of their babies had blue eyes. Deduce the genotypes of the lonely Quoll, his beautiful mate, and their babies.

5. In humans the ability to taste phenylthiourea depends on the presence of a dominant allele. The gene is not sex linked.
   a. Construct a pedigree chart to show a homozygous taster man and a non-taster woman and their two children, one son and one daughter.
   b. Their son marries a person of the same genotype for this gene. Continue the pedigree chart to show this and their three children, a son and two daughters. Each child has a different genotype.

6. Grandpa has blood group O. His first child, Horace, married a group O woman and they had two children, Belinda and Bertha, who were both group B.
   Grandpa's second child was group A, but the third child in the family, Clint, was group O. Grandpa thought it wise to tell his children before they studied this revision guide that the third child had been adopted.
   a. Deduce Granny's genotype showing all your reasoning.
   b. Why did Grandpa decide to say that Clint was adopted?

7. Web feet is a sex linked characteristic in Dingbats. Female Dingbats are XX and males XY. A webbed male is crossed with a homozygous normal female and the baby Dingbat is a female with normal feet.
Deduce whether the web allele is dominant or recessive.
If their next baby is a male determine whether it will have web or normal feet.

8. A plant breeder crossed a Pogwort with red flowers with one with white flowers and all the offspring were pink. Determine the flower colours and proportions of the F_2 generation.

Self-test Quiz

1. A gene can best be described as:
   a. a heritable factor that consists of a length of DNA,
   b. part of a chromosome,
   c. a homologous pair of alleles,
   d. a sequence of bases on an RNA molecule.

2. With sex-linked (X-linked) genes:
   a. both males and females are carriers,
   b. only males are affected,
   c. only females are carriers,
   d. only twins are affected.

3. A haploid cell is one in which:
   a. only one of each pair of chromosomes is present,
   b. there are 23 pairs of chromosomes,
   c. the sex chromosomes are missing,
   d. there is no nucleus.

4. Sickle cell anaemia is:
   a. a human genetic disease caused by an extra chromosome 21,
   b. a genetic disease only inherited by a son from his father,
   c. caused by the production of a faulty protein,
   d. due to non-disjunction.

5. The probability that a family of four children born to the same parents consists only of boys is:
   a. a quarter,
   b. a half,
   c. an eighth,
   d. a sixteenth.

6. A mother of a child is blood group A and the father is blood group B. The child could have blood group:
   a. A,
   b. B,
   c. A or B.
   d. A, B, AB, or O.

7. A father has one copy of the allele for Huntingdon's disease and the mother no copies. What is the probability that their second child will have the allele?
   a. an eighth,
   b. a quarter,
   c. a half,
   d. zero.

8. Cystic fibrosis is caused by:
   a. a dominant gene mutation,
   b. a recessive gene mutation,
   c. a base substitution mutation,
   d. a sex linked gene.

9. Sickle cell anaemia is caused by:
   a. a dominant gene mutation,
   b. a chromosome mutation,
   c. a base substitution mutation,
   d. a sex linked gene.

10. Two chromosomes that carry the same genes but not necessarily the same alleles are called:
   a. homozygous chromosomes,
   b. homologous chromosomes,
   c. sex chromosomes,
   d. codominant chromosomes.

11. A woman has one haemophilia allele and one normal allele. Which of the following statements is true?
   a. She is a carrier for the haemophilia allele.
   b. She will develop haemophilia.
   c. The probability of passing the haemophilia allele to her sons is 100%.
   d. All of her daughters will have the same genotype as herself.

12. A man has a sex linked recessive allele. His wife does not. What is the probability that their second son will also have the sex linked recessive allele?
   a. 100%,
   b. 75%,
   c. 25%,
   d. 0%.

13. A woman is homozygous for a recessive allele found on chromosome 20. Her husband is heterozygous. The probability that she will have a son who is also heterozygous is
   a. 50%,
   b. 0%,
   c. 25%,
   d. 75%.

14. Autosomes are:
   a. those chromosomes that carry homologous genes,
   b. those chromosomes that do not determine the sex of the individual,
   c. those chromosomes that do determine the sex of the individual,
   d. the only chromosomes that can carry out the process of crossing over.

15. A pedigree chart is used to show:
   a. if an allele is sex linked,
   b. if an allele is dominant or recessive,
   c. genetic relationships within a family tree.
   d. genetic relationships between different families.

16. Alleles are best described as:
   a. different genes,
   b. genes found on different chromosomes,
   c. different forms of a gene,
   d. genes only found on homologous chromosomes.

17. Haemophilia is caused by:
   a. a dominant gene mutation,
   b. non-disjunction,
   c. a base substitution mutation,
   d. a sex linked gene.

Chapter Eight

Evolution and Biodiversity

The theory of evolution was put forward at nearly the same time by Charles Darwin and Alfred Russel Wallace and was the most outstanding biological theory of the 19th century. Biodiversity is of tremendous importance at the present time given the global damage to habitats by humans.

Evolution

Charles Darwin and Alfred Russel Wallace

Charles Darwin joined HMS Beagle under Captain FitzRoy as the ship's naturalist. The ship sailed from Devonport 18th December 1831 on its 5 year mapping voyage for the British Admiralty.

9.1a

At every opportunity Darwin studied the plants, animals and geology of the places visited, sometimes leaving the ship for days and travelling overland. It was during this time that he began to formulate his ideas on variation. His observations on the tortoises and mocking birds of the Galapagos Islands reinforced these ideas and over the following 20 years at his house in Downe, Kent in the UK he accumulated more evidence and finally in 1859 published his book *On the Origin of Species by Means of Natural Selection*.

9.1b An elderly Charles Darwin

9.1c Beagle being hailed by native Fuegians during the survey of Tierra del Fuego, painted by Conrad Martens

Alfred Russel Wallace was a contemporary of Darwin and a great traveller, naturalist and collector. Extensive observations in the Amazon River basin and Malay Archipelago led him to the same conclusions as Darwin and in 1858 he published *On the Tendency of Varieties to Depart Indefinitely from the Original Type*. It was this which prompted Darwin to publish. The Wallace Line is a line running between Borneo and Sulawesi, and between the Indonesian islands of Bali and Lombok. The distance between these two islands is only about 35km yet Wallace observed a distinct difference in plant and animal species between them. To the West are Asiatic species and to the East a mix of Asiatic and Australian species. We now know that this is the junction between two tectonic plates and in the geological past the islands were a long distance apart.

9.2

Evolution by natural selection

Key steps
The Darwin–Wallace principle of evolution by natural selection

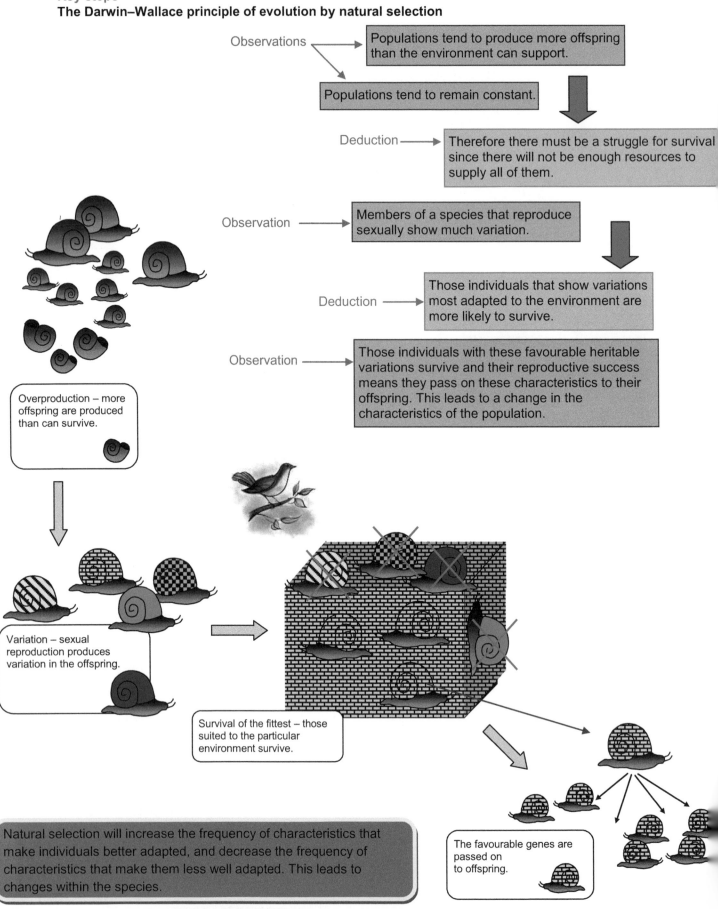

Observations → Populations tend to produce more offspring than the environment can support.

Populations tend to remain constant.

Deduction → Therefore there must be a struggle for survival since there will not be enough resources to supply all of them.

Observation → Members of a species that reproduce sexually show much variation.

Deduction → Those individuals that show variations most adapted to the environment are more likely to survive.

Observation → Those individuals with these favourable heritable variations survive and their reproductive success means they pass on these characteristics to their offspring. This leads to a change in the characteristics of the population.

Overproduction – more offspring are produced than can survive.

Variation – sexual reproduction produces variation in the offspring.

Survival of the fittest – those suited to the particular environment survive.

Natural selection will increase the frequency of characteristics that make individuals better adapted, and decrease the frequency of characteristics that make them less well adapted. This leads to changes within the species.

The favourable genes are passed on to offspring.

Variation

➢ The original source of variation is mutation which alters the genetic code.
➢ This variation is then shuffled around by:
   • crossing over during meiosis – see page 84,
   • random assortment during meiosis – see page 84,
   • random fertilisation.

Evolution in response to environmental change

• **Example 1 – Multiple antibiotic resistance in bacteria**

Methicillin-resistant *Staphylococcus aureus*, MRSA, and *Clostridium difficile* are two bacteria that have developed resistance and are a potential threat to human health.

Antibiotic destroys most bacteria. Those with resistance gene survive.

New antibiotic destroys most bacteria. Those with new resistance gene produced by mutation survive.

Asexual reproduction produces population all resistant to antibiotic.

Repeated use of new antibiotics results in multiple antibiotic resistance building up in the bacterial population. This is especially likely in hospitals.

Asexual reproduction produces population all resistant to both antibiotics.

• **Example 2 – Changes in finch beaks on the Galapagos**

General points

➢ The Galapagos Islands are a small group of 14 volcanic islands 926km west of Ecuador.
➢ A flock of finches from Ecuador were probably blown onto the islands in a storm many years ago.
➢ As the population expanded there would be competition for food.
➢ Natural variations in beak shapes and sizes would allow exploitation of the different food sources available.
➢ Over time this would lead to speciation – see page 196.

Charles Darwin visited the islands in 1835 on HMS Beagle. The 13 species of finches found amongst the islands are named after him.

The Island of Daphne Major

➢ This is a small, fairly isolated island susceptible to climate changes.
➢ Two species of finch, the large and medium ground finches, have been studied for many years by Peter and Rosemary Grant.

9.3a Medium ground finch. The beak is short and thick, ideal for small and medium seeds.

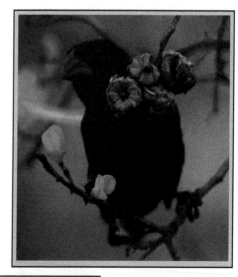

9.3b Large ground finch. The beak is better adapted for larger seeds.

- The original finch on the island was the medium ground finch.
- It had a range of beak sizes allowing it to exploit seeds of different sizes.
- In 1982 a few large ground finches flew to the island from a neighbouring one and fed on the larger seeds.
- Since the two species fed primarily on different sized seeds there was only a small level of competition between the large finch and any members of the medium finch population which had larger beaks.
- Two years of drought in 2003–4 drastically reduced plant growth and the lack of seeds caused both populations to fall dramatically.
- Medium finches with smaller beaks were able to find small seeds which finches with larger beaks could not pick up.
- Medium finches with large beaks were strongly competing for the larger seeds with the large finch.
- Smaller beaked birds survived better than larger beaked birds.
- A strong shift towards smaller beak size occurred with the medium finch in the following years, along with a change in foraging behaviour which focused towards smaller seeds.
- Thus there was an even greater divergence in beak size between the medium and large finches.

Evidence for evolution

1. Fossils

- The fossil remains of extinct species provide evidence that species are continuously evolving.
- Older rocks contain simpler organisms and species that are no longer living.
- Younger rocks contain species that resemble those that are alive today.
- It is not a perfect record of the evolution of species, but it does show that changes in species have taken place in the past.

9.4 Shell fossils   The first fossil is simply a print of a shell in mud which has hardened. In the other two the organism has been replaced with hard minerals.

2. Homologous structures

- These have the same evolutionary origin but now have different functions.
- Example – the pentadactyl limb.
- So called because it typically has five digits.
- Found in all four classes of vertebrates – amphibians, reptiles, birds and mammals.

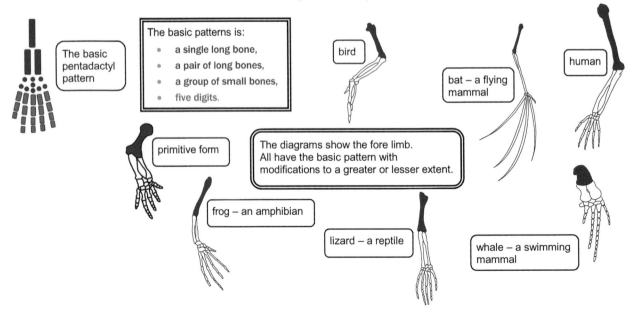

The basic pentadactyl pattern

The basic patterns is:
- a single long bone,
- a pair of long bones,
- a group of small bones,
- five digits.

bird

bat – a flying mammal

human

primitive form

The diagrams show the fore limb. All have the basic pattern with modifications to a greater or lesser extent.

frog – an amphibian

lizard – a reptile

whale – a swimming mammal

                    IBSL Biology 2016 © Ashby Merson-Davies

9.5 A bat wing

9.6 A Mesosaurus fossil from the early Permian 299-271mya. This clearly shows the pentadactyl limb.

3. Development of melanism in insects

➢ Example – The Peppered moth *Biston betularia*. This moth is common in England.
➢ The normal form has white wings covered in black specks.
➢ Dark forms in which the black specks had merged to varying degrees first appeared during the industrial revolution in the mid-19th century.
➢ The moth rests during the day on lichen covered tree trunks and the normal form would be well camouflaged.

dark form

normal form

On a lichen covered tree trunk the normal form is well camouflaged.

9.7 a

➢ As the trees near industrial areas became dirty with soot the dark forms would be camouflaged but the normal speckled form would be easily seen and eaten by birds.
➢ In clean country areas the dark form would be seen and eaten.
➢ As particular areas became industrialised the population of the dark form increased and that of the speckled form decreased.
➢ In 1956 the Clean Air Act was passed and gradually the soot was washed off the trees.
➢ Selection pressure started to work against the dark forms and over the next 30 years the speckled form became more common.

On a soot covered tree trunk the dark form is well camouflaged.

9.7b

9.7 The peppered moth

4. Selective breeding of domesticated animals

➢ Breeds have been produced for food production, working, pets, sport.
➢ Humans have selected a particular feature and used these animals to breed from.
➢ Offspring which showed an increase in this feature were bred from and the process repeated.
➢ Dogs – Chinese dog (food), sheep dog (working), dachshund (pet), greyhound (sport).
➢ Cattle – Jersey (milk), Aberdeen Angus (beef).
➢ If new varieties can be produced by Man selecting specific characteristics then the same can happen if the environment does the selecting.

9.8 Sheep dog

5. Continuous variation

➢ Gulls in the genus *Larus* can be found in a ring around the North Pole.

➢ It shows continuous variation of related populations across the geographical range.

➢ This matches the concept of gradual divergence.

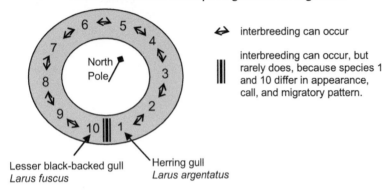

↔ interbreeding can occur

‖ interbreeding can occur, but rarely does, because species 1 and 10 differ in appearance, call, and migratory pattern.

Lesser black-backed gull
Larus fuscus

Herring gull
Larus argentatus

The original species probably spread in one direction (in the diagram this would be anticlockwise) and selection produced minor variations along the way. When the end of the ring closed back at the starting point there was so much variation between the starting form and the final form that interbreeding was inhibited.

Herring gull
Grey back and pink legs

Lesser black-backed gull. Black back. Winter adults have pink legs; summer adults have yellow legs.

9.9 The two gull species at the ends of the North Pole gull cline

Speciation

Key points

➢ A gene pool consists of all the genes and their different alleles present in an interbreeding population.

➢ Speciation occurs when populations of species gradually diverge into separate species by evolution.

➢ Natural selection acts on each population gene pool in a different way.

➢ Evolution requires that allele frequencies change with time in populations.

➢ The populations must be isolated in some way by a barrier.

➢ The barrier could be:

• geographical – a river or mountain range separates the populations,

• temporal – different populations are around at different times,

• behavioural – mating rituals or calls could be different in different populations.

• food – different populations prefer different foodplants,

• environmental – if different aspects of the environment favour one form over another.

➢ Speciation can be gradual or abrupt.

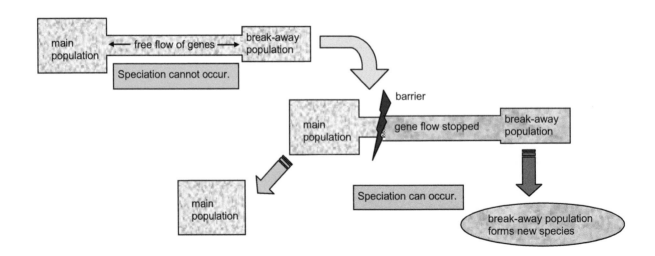

Sympatric speciation

This is speciation that occurs in the same geographical area. ('Sym' means 'together' as in sympathy.)

Plants on the western slope of a valley will get the sun in the early morning and those on the eastern slope will get it in the late afternoon. This could lead to different times for the flowers opening for pollination leading to *temporal* isolation of the two populations.

Allopatric speciation

This is speciation that occurs in different geographical areas.

A sharp meander in a river could break through leaving an oxbow lake or billabong with an island. Animals on the island that could not fly or swim would be *geographically* isolated from the surrounding populations.

The pace of evolution – gradualism and punctuated equilibrium

Gradualism

A slow change from one form to another.

Punctuated equilibrium

Long periods with little change with intermittent short periods of rapid change.

Points for discussion

➤ Gradualism is a Darwinian approach.
➤ The fossil record indicates this to be true in some cases, e.g. the horse leg where the fossils show all the stages from the earliest horse to the modern horse.
➤ In other cases the fossil record shows no intermediates.
➤ Eldredge and Gould proposed (1972) that most evolutionary changes take place at the time of speciation.
➤ Small populations that become isolated do not contain the full gene pool and have different allele frequencies.
➤ Environmental differences encourage rapid speciation in these small populations and once established new genotypes resist change.
➤ The population enters a long period of stasis until punctuated by another change.
➤ An example of this would be the variety of Darwin's finches on the volcanic Galapagos Islands.
➤ Sometimes these changes can affect local populations such as a rise in sea level creating an island, or a major volcanic eruption that affects the global climate, e.g. after Krakatoa erupted in 1883 average global temperatures fell by 1.2^0C.

9.10 Gradualism

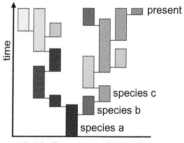

9.11 Punctuated equilibrium

Polyploidy

➤ This is having more than three sets of chromosomes in the nucleus.
➤ Polyploidy can result in self-sterility, e.g. meiosis in a triploid cell results in gametes with variable numbers of chromosomes because the chromosomes left over after pairs of homologous chromosomes have formed bivalents will end up randomly in the gametes.
➤ This results in reproductive isolation.

Polyploidy and speciation in Alliums

➤ The *Allium* genus includes onions, chives, leeks and garlic.
➤ They are highly variable in their chromosome numbers.
➤ Many *Allium* species reproduce asexually which, since it is done by mitosis, is not affected by chromosome numbers.

Some examples of Alliums

Species	2n	Ploidy level
A. aflatunense	16	2x
A. carinatum	16	2x
	24	3x
A. senescens	32	4x
A. oleraceum	40	5x
A. nutans	66	8x

Selection mechanisms

There are three categories of selection pressure:

- stabilising,
- directional,
- disruptive.

1. Stabilising

- Snail shells show a range of colours from very pale brown to dark brown.
- 'Forest snails' live in brown leaf litter.
- Snails with very pale or very dark shells can easily be seen by predators.
- Selection pressure will therefore favour mid brown shells.

2. Directional

- Mice normally have brown coloured fur.
- The fur colour will show a range from very pale brown to dark brown.
- 'Beach mice' live on white sand dunes.
- Dark coloured mice can easily be seen by predators.
- Selection pressure will therefore favour pale fur.

3. Disruptive

- The Peppered moth (see page 195) has white wings speckled with black.
- The amount of black speckling shows variation.
- Moths with lightly speckled wings survive best in clean countryside.
- Moths with heavy speckling survive best in countryside that has been polluted with soot from chimneys.
- This splits the mixed population.

IBSL Biology 2016 © Ashby Merson-Davies

1a. What is the original source of genetic variation?	1b. List three ways that this genetic variation can be shuffled around.	2. What is the principle behind using fossils as evidence for evolution?
3a. What are homologous structures?	3b. State an example of homologous structures.	4. What is the name given to the development of black pigmentation in response to soot pollution?
5a. Name the process where a new species develops from an existing one.	5b. What key feature must exist for this to occur?	6. List the three types of selection mechanism.

Classification of biodiversity

Classification
Key points

➤ Organisms are grouped into three domains.

The 3 Domains

Eubacteria   **Archaea**   **Eukaryota**

> All prokaryotic organisms (those without a true nucleus) used to be grouped together as 'bacteria'. In 1977 Carl Woese sequenced ribosomal RNA and discovered that one group of 'bacteria' were so different from the others that he proposed the three domain system. In fact the Archaea share many molecular features with the Eukaryota, e.g. their DNA is associated with histones.

➤ The Eukaryotes include protoctistans, fungi, plants and animals.
➤ Classification of an organism is done by putting it into a hierarchy of taxa.
➤ The genus and accompanying higher taxa contain all the species that have evolved from a single ancestral common species.
➤ Taxonomists sometimes reclassify groups of species when new evidence shows that a previous taxon contains species that have evolved from different ancestral species.
➤ A natural classification can help in identification of species and allow the prediction of characteristics shared by species within a group.

> **Natural classification:**
> This is classifying an organism based on its evolutionary relationships, i.e. kingdom to species.
> **Artificial classification:**
> This is sometimes used to group organisms which show similar characteristics due to convergent evolution, e.g. all organisms with wings.

The hierarchy of taxa

Kingdom
Phylum
Class
Order
Family
Genus
Species

One way to remember this is:
King
Philip
Classified
Over
Fifty
Green
Spiders

Examples

Taxonomic rank	Plant example	Animal example
Domain	Eukaryota	Eukaryota
Kingdom	Plantae	Animalia
Phylum	Angiospermophyta	Chordata
Class	Dicotyledonaea	Mammalia
Order	Ranales	Primates
Family	Ranunculacae	Hominidae
Genus	*Ranunculus*	*Homo*
Species	*acris*	*sapiens*
Common name	Meadow buttercup	Human

The binomial system

Key points

➤ Each organism has two Latin names, its genus and species.

It is typed in italics but when hand-written it is underlined

Homo sapiens = modern humans.

The genus starts with a capital letter

The species starts with a small letter

Other examples used so far in this chapter:

Large ground finch – *Geospiza magnirostris*
Medium ground finch – *Geospiza fortis*
Peppered moth – *Biston betularia*
Lesser black-backed gull – *Larus fuscus*
Herring gull – *Larus argentatus*

Darwin was especially fascinated by beetles and 71 species are named after him. In 2002 a small moth discovered on the Galapagos island of San Cristobal was named *Galagete darwini*.

➤ The system is international.
➤ Names are agreed at congresses.
➤ All biologists use the same names.
➤ Misunderstandings through language differences are prevented.
➤ The first name is the genus name and shows which other species are closely related.

Plants

Group	Recognition Features
Bryophyta Mosses and Liverworts	No roots or cuticle. No vascular system. Rhizoids similar to root hairs. Mosses with simple leaf-like structures. Liverworts have flattened shape called a thallus. Spores produced in capsules.
Filicinophyta Ferns	Roots. Leaves in fronds. Cuticle on leaves. Simple vascular tissue. Can form small trees, but not woody. Spores produced in structures called sporangia on the underside of the fronds (second photo).
Coniferophyta Conifers	Shrubs to very large trees. Roots, stems, leaves. Woody stems and roots. Produce pollen and ovules in cones. Produce seeds. Vascular tissue more advanced than the Filicinophyta.
Angiospermophyta Flowering plants	Highly variable in structure – tiny herbaceous to large trees. Roots, stems, leaves, flowers. Can form woody tissue. Some parasitic. Produce pollen and ovules in flowers. Produce seeds. Fruits often produced for seed dispersal. Well formed vascular tissue.

9.12a   9.12b

9.12c

9.12d

9.12e

9.12f

9.12 Major plant groups

Animals

Group	Recognition Features
Porifera Sponges	No special shape. No mouth or anus. Lack tissues and organs. Collection of cells of different types organised into pores, canals and chambers.
Cnidaria Jellyfish, sea anemones and corals.	Two cell layers. Radial symmetry. Mouth. Two forms – medusa (jellyfish) and polyp (sea anemone). Some corals have hard calcareous cover. Tentacles with stinging cells.
Platyhelminthes Flatworms, flukes, tapeworms	Flat and unsegmented. Bilateral symmetry. Mouth but no anus. Rudimentary head. No vascular system.
Mollusca Snails, slugs, squids, octopus	Soft, flexible body with no obvious segmentation. Head, muscular foot and visceral hump. Hard rasping radula for feeding. Many with a single or double shell. Open circulatory system with simple heart.
Annelida Segmented worms, leeches	Segmented body. Bilateral symmetry. Mouth and anus. Vascular system with simple heart. Bristles (chaetae).
Arthropoda Crabs, spiders, scorpions, centipedes, insects	Segmented. Bilateral symmetry. Hard exoskeleton made of chitin. Jointed appendages. Vascular system with simple heart. Most land species have a system of tubes (trachea) throughout the body for gas exchange.
Chordata Fish, amphibians, reptiles, birds, mammals.	Segmented. Bilateral symmetry. Endoskeleton of cartilage or bone. Well-developed vascular and gas exchange systems.

13a

13b

9.13c

9.13d

9.13e

9.13f

9.13g

9.13h

9.13 Major animal groups

Vertebrate animals

Group	Recognition Features
Fish	Mostly fully aquatic. Gas exchange through gills. Scaly skin. Skeleton of cartilage or bone. No limbs. External fertilisation. Ectothermic.
Amphibians Frogs, toads, newts, salamanders.	Land living but usually requiring a moist habitat. Simple lungs for gas exchange. Some use a moist skin for additional gas exchange. Adults with four limbs. External fertilisation. Aquatic gill breathing juvenile stages. Show metamorphosis. Ectothermic.
Reptiles Snakes, lizards, iguanas, chameleons, turtles, tortoises, crocodilians.	Mostly land living. Lungs for gas exchange. Dry scaly skin. Internal fertilisation. Eggs have a tough leathery coat. Ectothermic.
Birds	Skin with feathers. Scaly legs. Horny beak. Wings. Well-developed lungs. Internal fertilisation. Eggs have a hard calcareous shell. Endothermic.
Mammals	Skin with fur / hair. Well-developed lungs. Teeth. Internal fertilisation. Young develop internally. Produce milk from mammary glands. Endothermic.

9.14a

9.14b

9.14c

9.14c

9.14e

9.14 Major vertebrate groups

A dichotomous key

Key points

➢ Dichotomous means two, therefore each step is a pair of statements, and the number to the right directs you to the next pair.

➢ Each statement must be qualitative and not relative, e.g. 'long leaf blade' is meaningless but 'length of leaf blade greater than width' can be measured.

Example

1. Leaf with toothed margin ………………………….…………… 2
   Leaf with smooth margin ……………………………………… 15
2. Lateral veins branch off midrib alternately left and right ……… 3
   Lateral veins branch off midrib in pairs ………………………… 7
3. Tip of leaf blade rounded ……………………………………… apple
   Tip of leaf blade pointed ……………………………………… 10

©Ashby Merson-Davies

7. List the three domains.	8. List the hierarchy of taxa.	9. Which taxa are used in the binomial system?
10. List 4 advantages to scientists of the binomial system.		11. Which group of plants have leaves in fronds and a simple vascular system?
	12. Which group of plants have flowers?	13. Which group of plants produce seeds in cones?
14. Which group of animals have flat and unsegmented bodies and bilateral symmetry?	15. Which group of animals have a head, muscular foot and visceral hump?	16. Which group of animals have gills and use external fertilisation?
17. Which group of animals have jointed limbs and an exoskeleton?	18. Which group of animals are radially symmetrical and have tentacles with stinging cells?	19. Which group of animals are segmented and have an endoskeleton of cartilage or bone?
20. Which group of animals have scaly legs and a skin with feathers?	21. Which group of animals are segmented, have bristles, a mouth and anus?	22. Which group of animals have no special shape and are simply collections of cells lacking tissue organisation?
23. Which group of animals have a dry scaly skin and use lungs?	24. Which group of animals have simple lungs, external fertilisation and an aquatic juvenile stage?	25. Which group of animals have skin with hair, internal fertilisation and young that develop internally?

Clades, cladistics and cladograms

Definitions
Clade
➤ All of the organisms, both living and fossil, descended from a common ancestor.

Cladistics
➤ A method of classifying living organisms based on the construction and analysis of cladograms.

Cladogram
➤ An evolutionary tree showing points at which clades diverged from a common ancestral form.
➤ Evidence comes from biochemical data:
  • number of differences in the DNA base sequence of a gene, or
  • number of differences in the amino acid sequence of a protein.
➤ Sequence differences accumulate gradually.
➤ Thus there is a positive correlation between the number of differences between two species and the time difference since they diverged from a common ancestor.

Cladogram terms
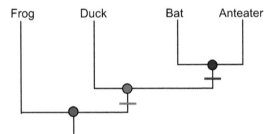

➤ The coloured circles where the tree branches are called **nodes**.
➤ Groups of organisms that share a common ancestor form a **clade**.
➤ This is easily seen with the 'snip rule'.
➤ The bat and anteater form a clade if you snip at the blue line.
➤ The duck, bat and anteater form a clade if you snip at the orange line.
➤ The duck and bat do not form a clade because snipping at the orange line means the anteater falls off as well and must therefore be included.

Cladogram structure
Key points
➤ The pattern of branching in a cladogram aims to match the evolutionary origins of each species.
➤ The sequence of splits at nodes indicates when species diverged.
➤ Clades connected to a single node are more closely related than clades connected via two or more nodes.
➤ The length of the branches in morphological cladograms is arbitrary and does not show evolutionary distances.
➤ The length of the branches in biochemical cladograms sometimes shows evolutionary distances based on the number of changes.

IBSL Biology 2016 © Ashby Merson-Davies

Constructing a cladogram using biochemical data
Example 1
The table shows the number of amino acid differences between the human haemoglobin beta chain and a number of other animals.

Human	horse	grey kangaroo	cow	gorilla	rhesus monkey
0	25	38	25	1	8

Rearrange the data into descending order.

grey kangaroo	horse	cow	rhesus monkey	gorilla	human
38	25	25	8	1	0

Assuming that the rate of change is constant a cladogram can be drawn to scale.

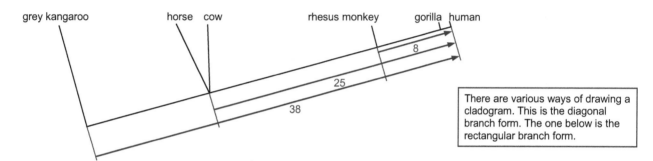

There are various ways of drawing a cladogram. This is the diagonal branch form. The one below is the rectangular branch form.

Example 2

Number of nucleotide substitutions	chimpanzee	gorilla	orangutan	gibbon	Japanese macaque	rhesus monkey
human	0.094	0.110	0.179	0.205	0.268	0.271
chimpanzee		0.113	0.192	0.214	0.285	0.298
gorilla			0.189	0.215	0.274	0.271
orangutan				0.211	0.289	0.292
gibbon					0.293	0.280
Japanese macaque						0.037

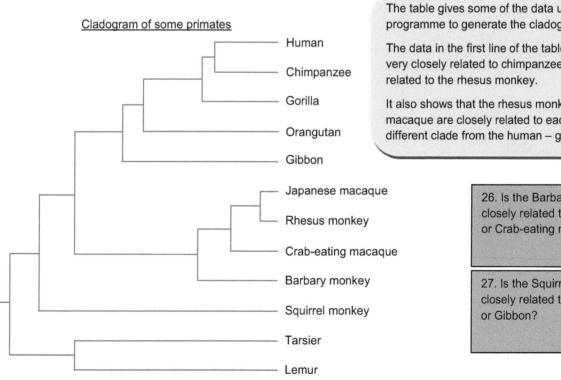

Cladogram of some primates

The table gives some of the data used by a computer programme to generate the cladogram.

The data in the first line of the table shows that humans are very closely related to chimpanzees and most distantly related to the rhesus monkey.

It also shows that the rhesus monkey and Japanese macaque are closely related to each other but on a different clade from the human – gibbon clade.

26. Is the Barbary monkey more closely related to the Rhesus monkey or Crab-eating macaque?

27. Is the Squirrel monkey more closely related to the Rhesus monkey or Gibbon?

Example 3

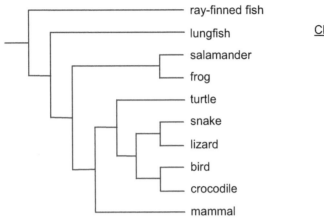

Cladogram of some vertebrate groups

| 28. Do the snake and lizard form a clade? |
| 29. Do the lizard and bird form a clade? |
| 30. Do the ray-finned fish and lungfish form a clade? |
| 31. Do the snake, lizard, bird and crocodile form a clade? |

Homologous and analogous characteristics

Homologous characteristics
Ones that share a common evolutionary origin but do not necessarily have the same function now.
Examples:
- bird wing and bat wing,
- human arm and horse front leg,
- whale flipper and chimpanzee arm.

Analogous characteristics
Ones which now have a similar function but different evolutionary origins.
Examples:
- bird wing and butterfly wing,
- wasp eye and octopus eye,
- beetle leg and cat leg.

Reclassifying organisms using cladistics

➤ Up until towards the end of the 20th Century classification was based primarily on morphological characteristics.

➤ A natural classification should be based on homologous characteristics.

➤ Analogous characteristics can cause confusion and muddle the true classification.

➤ Analysis of DNA base and amino acid sequences allowed biochemical cladograms to be drawn.

➤ This resulted in the reclassification of several groups, some being merged, others divided, and sometimes species moving from one group to another.

Example – the Figwort family, *Scrophulariaceae*
This family has a worldwide distribution but no clearly defined traits that could be used for classification, so more and more plants were added resulting in a rather mixed collection of some 5000 species in over 270 genera.
Analysis of three chloroplast genes indicated several clades had been wrongly included in the family.

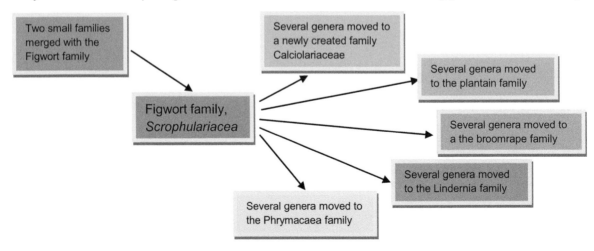

Glossary

Bilateral symmetry	Left and right sides of an organism when divided down the back are mirror images.
Endothermic	Regulating body temperature using heat generated internally.
Ectothermic	Regulating body temperature using heat from the sun.
Metamorphosis	Changing body form through juvenile stages to an adult.
Ploidy	The number of sets of chromosomes in a nucleus. Haploid = 1 set, diploid = 2 sets, polyploidy = 3 or more sets.
Radial symmetry	The two halves of a body are mirror images regardless of the angle of the cut through the centre.

Answers to Grey Box Questions

1a. Mutation.

1b. Crossing-over; random assortment / alignment; random fertilisation.

2. Older rocks contain older fossils.

3a. Structures that have the same evolutionary origin but may not have the same function.

3b. Pentadactyl limb.   4. (Industrial) melanism.

5a. Speciation.   5b. Isolating barrier.

6. Stabilising; directional; disruptive.   7. Eubacteria; Archaea; Eukarya.

8. Kingdom; phylum; class; order; family; genus; species.   9. Genus + species.

10. The system is international.

Names are agreed at congresses.

All biologists use the same names.

Misunderstandings through language differences are prevented.

The first name is the genus name and shows which other species are closely related.

11. Filicinophyta.	12. Angiospermophyta.	13. Coniferophyta.
14. Platyhelminthes.	15. Mollusca.	16. Fish.
17. Arthropoda.	18. Cnidaria.	19. Chordata.
20. Birds.	21. Annelida.	22. Porifera.
23. Reptiles.	24. Amphibia.	25. Mammals.
26. Crab-eating macaque.		27. Gibbon.
28. Yes.	29. No. 30. Yes.	31. No

Self-test Quiz

1. Use the key to identify the leaf.
   1 leaf margin even.....................................2
     leaf margin wavy.....................................oak
   2 veins branch off central vein in pairs..............5
     veins branch off alternately left and right........3
   3 tip of leaf blade rounded........................... lilac
     tip of leaf blade pointed............................4
   4 leaf margin smooth..................................beech
     leaf margin toothed..................................rose

© Ashby Merson-Davies

oak	lilac	beech	rose
a.	b.	c.	d.

2. Which of the following is a correct sequence for the hierarchy of taxa?
   a. Phylum, class, genus, family,
   b. Phylum, family, order, genus,
   c. Class, order, genus, species,
   d. Class, phylum, genus, species.

3. Which of the following is the correct definition of evolution?
   a. A change in the heritable characteristics of a population.
   b. An increase in the mutation rate of a population.
   c. A high level of selection pressure on a population.
   d. The selection of a specific desirable characteristic in an individual.

4. The greenhouse effect is due to:
   a. the accumulation of dust in the atmosphere,
   b. an increase in the heat output of the sun,
   c. an increase in heat output due to the rise in human population,
   d. a decrease in the proportion of solar energy radiated back into space from the earth's atmosphere.

5. Which of the following factors is **least** likely to bring about a reduction in global warming:
   a. using natural gas rather than oil as a source of energy,
   b. consuming only food grown in the country of origin,
   c. increased use of renewable energy sources,
   d. recycling organic waste materials as a manure.

6. Which of the following are greenhouse gases?
   a. water, methane, carbon dioxide, hydrogen,
   b. nitrogen oxide, carbon dioxide, oxygen,
   c. methane, carbon dioxide, nitrogen oxide,
   d. nitrogen oxide, water, methane, oxygen.

7. In the binomial system of classification:
   a. all organisms are divided into two groups,
   b. all organisms have two names representing the genus and the species,
   c. all organisms have two names representing the family and the species,
   d. organisms are always arranged in pairs.

8. Darwin and Wallace made the following observations in support of their theory of natural selection.
   'Populations tend to produce more offspring than the environment can support'.
   'Populations tend to remain constant.'
   What was their deduction from these observations?
   a. The populations would produce fewer offspring.
   b. The populations would migrate to regions with more resources.
   c. Resources within the ecosystem would increase to support the larger populations.
   d. Individuals within the populations would find it difficult to survive.

9. Multiple antibiotic resistance in bacteria arises due to:
   a. repeated exposure of the bacteria to a range of antibiotics,
   b. repeated exposure of the bacteria to a specific antibiotic,
   c. patients spending too long in hospitals where antibiotics are used,
   d. use of antibiotics after their 'use by' date.

10. Darwin's finches on the Galapagos Islands show a range of beak shapes and sizes. Which of the following reasons would **not** be an explanation for this?
    a. There was competition for food resources.
    b. Selection pressure eliminated unsuitable beak shapes.
    c. There was a range of food sources available on the islands.
    d. There was completion for nesting sites.

11. Homologous structures are best described as:
    a. structures which have the same function but different origins,
    b. structures which have the same origin and the same functions,
    c. structures which have the same origin but different functions,
    d. structures which all look the same.

12. Which of the following statements about speciation is correct?
    a.   Development of new species as a result of populations becoming isolated from each other.
    b.   Development of new species due to mutations arising in the original population.
    c.   Development of new species as a result of two isolated populations merging together.
    d.   Development of new species due to a population moving to a different habitat.

13. Which one of the following graphs indicates that directional selection pressure has occurred, assuming the original population had a normal distribution of the characteristic?

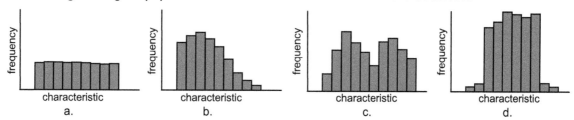

14. Which of the following groups do jellyfish belong to?
    a.   fish,
    b.   mollusca,
    c.   porifera,
    d.   cnidaria.

15. Which of the following groups do ferns belong to?
    a.   coniferophyta,
    b.   bryophyte,
    c.   angiospermophyta,
    d.   filicinophyta.

16. Which of the following groups do snails and squids belong to?
    a.   arthropoda,
    b.   mollusca,
    c.   annelida,
    d.   chordata.

17. Which of the following groups do crabs and insects belong to?
    a.   arthropoda,
    b.   cnidarian,
    c.   porifera,
    d.   platyhelminthes.

18. Which of the following groups shows radial symmetry?
    a.   annelida,
    b.   arthropoda,
    c.   mollusca,
    d.   cnidaria.

19. Which of the following groups does not have a vascular system?
    a.   filicinophyta,
    b.   bryophyta,
    c.   angiospermophyta,
    d.   coniferophyta.

20. Which of the following groups have a dry scaly skin and lay eggs with a leathery coat?
    a.   reptiles,
    b.   amphibians,
    c.   birds,
    d.   chordates.

Appendix 1

Answers to Self-test Quizzes

Chapter 1

1. d.
2. a. 7500x. b. 7000x. c. 5000x.
3. a. 11mm. b. 200mm. c. 62μm.
4. Mean = 1.72m. Median = 1.65m. Mode = 1.6m
5. $\frac{23}{47}$ × 100 = 49% increase.
6. $\frac{85}{85}$ = 1 $\frac{376}{85}$ = 4.4   Ratio = 1 : 4.4
7. Mean 13mm. Standard deviation 1.6mm.

Don't forget the units

8. Negative.

Variable A

Variable B

9. She was right to say the standard deviation was small but not very small. 33% of 47 is 15.5 and 13 is very close to this , so it is actually close to being a large standard deviation.
10. a.
11. c.
12. b.
13. d.

14a.

Number of quadrats	Number of quadrats		Row totals
	Moss present	**Moss absent**	
Liverwort present	120	29	149
Liverwort absent	46	5	51
Column totals	166	34	**Grand total** 200

14b.

Number of quadrats	Number of quadrats		Row totals
	Moss present	**Moss absent**	
Liverwort present	123.7	25.3	149
Liverwort absent	42.3	8.7	51
Column totals	166	34	**Grand total** 200

14c. One.

14d. Chi-squared = 2.51. The critical value for 5% is 2.84. The calculated value is less than this and so the null hypothesis is accepted – there is no association between the moss and liverwort.

15.

a. 56% / 57% ⋯⋯⋯⋯⋯⋯⋯⋯⋯⋯⋯⋯
b. 8^{0}C to 25^{0}C is a rise of 17^{0}C.

—·—·—·—·—·—·—

16. d.
17. c.
18. a.

Chapters 2–8

	Chapter							5			
	2 Part 1	2 Part 2	3	4	6	7	8				
1	d	b	d	c	b	a	c	**Digestion**		**Defence**	
2	d	a	d	a	d	c	c	1	c	1	d
3	b	b	b	b	c	a	a	2	a	2	c
4	d	d	a	c	d	c	d	3	a	3	a
5	c	a	c	d	b	d	a	4	b	4	c
6	c	b	a	c	a	d	c	5	d	5	c
7	b	d	c	b	a	c	b	6	d	6	a
8	c	a	b	d	c	b	d	7	a	**Nervous system**	
9	b	b	a	c	d	c	a	8	b	1	b
10	a	c	a	d	b	b	d	9	b	2	d
11	b	d	d	a	c	a	c	**Gas exchange**		3	c
12	d	d	d	c	a	d	a	1	a	4	a
13	a	a	a	d	d	c	b	2	c	5	a
14	a	c	c	a	b	b	d	3	d	6	b
15	d	b	d	b	a	c	d	4	c	7	d
16	c	d	d		c	c	b	5	a	8	b
17	a	d	a		d	d	a	6	d	**Endocrine system**	
18	c	c	d		b		d	7	b	1	a
19	b	a	c		a		b	8	d	2	c
20	c		a		b		a	**Blood system**		3	d
21			c					1	d	4	b
22			d					2	c	5	a
23			c					3	d	6	c
24			c					4	a	7	c
25			a					5	b	**Reproduction**	
26			a					6	c	1	b
27			d					7	c	2	c
28			b					8	a	3	a
29			d					9	b	4	c
30			c					10	d	5	d
31			b					11	a	6	a
32			a					12	a	7	a
33			a					13	d	8	c
								14	b		
								15	a		

Appendix 2

Answers to Chapter 7 (Genetics) Test Problems

1. The majority of all the young mice is black so that tells us that black is dominant. The grey male mouse must be homozygous recessive. Since about half the offspring of the first black female are grey she must have the grey allele in her genotype. Thus she is heterozygous. The second female only produces black offspring and so, given the numbers, it is likely that she is homozygous black.

    Key: B = black; b = grey.

		black female A	x	grey male	x	black female B
P		Bb		bb		BB
G₁		(B) (b)		(b)		(B)

F₁

	B	b
b	Bb	bb
	black	grey

	B
b	Bb
	black

2. The F₁ Bandycoot babies were all yellow but orange ones appeared in the F₂. This tells us that yellow must be dominant and orange recessive. The test for heterozygosity is a test cross, that is with the homozygous recessive. A homozygous dominant genotype will not give any orange offspring whereas about half the offspring will be orange with a heterozygous genotype.

    Key: Y = yellow; y = orange.

		heterozygous Bandycoot	x	orange Bandycoot	x	homozygous Bandycoot
P		Yy		yy		YY
G₁		(Y) (y)		(y)		(Y)

F₁

	Y	y
y	Yy	yy
	50% yellow	50% orange

	Y
y	Yy
	All yellow

3. We are told that green is dominant.
    Key: G = green; g = blue.
    The blue-eyed beetle must therefore have the genotype gg. Its parents were both green-eyed and either had the genotype GG or Gg. However since the beetle must inherit one allele from each parent both parents must be Gg.
    The female beetle is green eyed but the first baby Boring beetle is blue eyed. Hence her genotype must be Gg.
    If they have another baby beetle it could be green-eyed with the genotype Gg.

P		green-eyed parent Gg	green-eyed parent Gg
G₁		(G) (g)	(G) (g)

F₁

	G	g
G		
g		gg
		blue-eyed beetle

P		blue-eyed beetle gg	green-eyed beetle Gg
G₁		(g)	(G) (g)

F₁

	g
G	Gg
	green eyes
g	gg
	blue eyes

> Note how the Punnett grids are big enough to include the phenotypes. This is a quicker and more accurate / efficient way of linking genotype and phenotype.

4. Since all the first generation Quolls had luminous eyes, luminous must be dominant. Furthermore since the first generation did not contain any blue-eyed Quolls we can assume that the luminous-eyed parent was homozygous.

Key: L = luminous and l = blue.

P   luminous eyes   blue eyes
           LL   ll

G₁   L   l

F₁
	l
L	Ll
	luminous eyes

These offspring all met luminous-eyed Quolls and since their offspring were also all luminous-eyed we can again assume they were homozygous, LL.

P   luminous eyes   luminous eyes
           LL   Ll

G₁   L   L   l

F₁
	l
L	Ll
	luminous eyes
l	ll
	blue eyes

Lonely Quoll though met a blue-eyed Quoll, and since blue eyes must have the genotype ll this would produce 50% blue-eyed offspring.

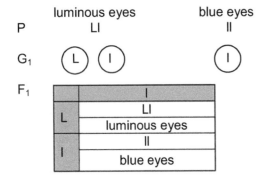

P   luminous eyes   blue eyes
           Ll   ll

G₁   L   l   l

F₁
	l
L	Ll
	luminous eyes
l	ll
	blue eyes

5.

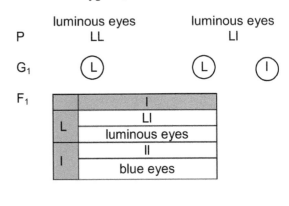

Homozygous taster	■
Homozygous non-taster	○
Heterozygous taster	◉ ▣

6. If Grandpa was blood group O then his genotype had to be ii. His son Horace married a person who was also group O and therefore genotype ii. Their two daughters were group B and this I^B allele therefore had to have come from their father Horace. This meant that his genotype was I^B?, but since his father could only have given him an i allele we can deduce his genotype was $I^B i$. This means that the I^B allele must have come from his mother, making her genotype I^B?. Grandpa's second child was group A, and using a similar argument we can deduce that the I^A allele must have come from Grandma. Finally therefore we can deduce that Grandma's genotype was $I^A I^B$ and hence her blood group AB.
This therefore makes it impossible for Grandpa and Grandma to have a group O child – all their children have to be either group A or group B.

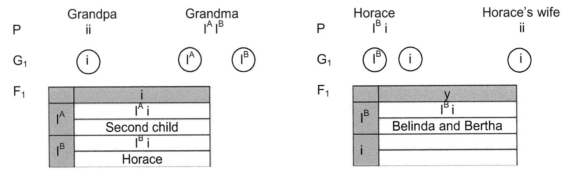

P   Grandpa   Grandma   P   Horace   Horace's wife
           ii $I^A I^B$ $I^B i$ ii

G₁   i I^A I^B G₁ I^B i   i

F₁   F₁
	i			y
-----	---		-----	---
I^A	$I^A i$		I^B	$I^B i$
	Second child			Belinda and Bertha
I^B	$I^B i$		i	
	Horace			

7. We are told the characteristic is sex linked. Female Dingbats are XX and the males XY. The baby Dingbat is a female and therefore inherited one of her X chromosomes from the father. This chromosome carried the web allele, and her other X chromosome from her mother carried the normal allele. Since baby has normal feet we can deduce that normal is dominant. Males always inherit their X chromosome from their mother, and since both her X chromosomes carry the normal allele he too will have normal feet.

Key : N = normal feet, n = webbed feet.

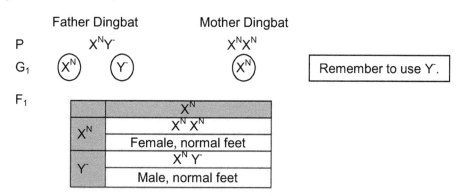

Remember to use Y^-.

8. Since the offspring were all pink this tells us that the Pogwort flower colour genes are codominant. The red and white flowered parents therefore had to be homozygous.

Key: C^R = red, C^W = white

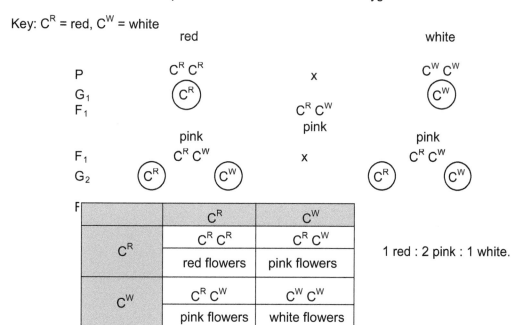

1 red : 2 pink : 1 white.

Appendix 3

External Assessment Specifications

Component	Overall weighting %	Duration hours	Format and syllabus coverage
Paper 1	20	¾	30 multiple choice questions.
Paper 2	40	1¼	Section A One data-based question and several short-answer questions (all compulsory). Section B **One** extended response questions from a choice of two.
Paper 3	20	1	Section A Two or three short answer questions based on experimental skills and techniques, analysis and evaluation using unseen data linked to the core material. Section B Short answer and extended response questions from **one Option**.

Appendix 4

Objective 1

Define	Give precise meaning of a word or phrase as concisely as possible.
Draw	Represent by means of pencil lines (add labels unless told not to do so.
Label	Add labels to diagrams.
List	Give a sequence of names or other brief answers with no elaboration, each one clearly separated from the others.
Measure	Find a value for a quantity.
State	Give a specific name, value or other brief answer (no supporting argument or calculation is necessary).

Objective 2

Annotate	Add brief notes to a diagram, drawing or graph.
Apply	Use an idea, equation, principle, theory or law in a new situation.
Calculate	Find an answer using mathematical methods (show the working unless instructed no to do so).
Describe	Give a detailed account, including all the relevant information.
Distinguish	Give the differences between two or more different items.
Estimate	Find an approximate value for an unknown quantity based on the information provided and scientific knowledge.
Identify	Find an answer from a number of possibilities.
Outline	Give a brief account or summary (include essential information only).

Objective 3

Analyse	Interpret data to reach conclusions.
Comment	Give a judgement based on a given statement or result of a calculation.
Compare and Contrast	Give an account of similarities and differences between two (or more) items, referring to both (all) of them throughout (comparisons can be given using a table).
Construct	Represent or develop in graphical form.
Deduce	Reach a conclusion from the information given.
Derive	Manipulate a mathematical equation to give a new equation or result.
Design	Produce a plan, object, simulation or model.
Determine	Find the only possible answer.
Discuss	Give an account including, where possible, a range of arguments, assessments of the relative importance of various factors or comparisons of alternative hypotheses.
Evaluate	Assess the implications and limitations.
Explain	Give a clear account including causes, reasons or mechanisms.
Predict	Give an expected result.
Show	Give the steps in a calculation or derivation.
Sketch	Represent by means of a graph showing a line and labelled but unscaled axes but with important features (for example, intercept) clearly indicated.
Solve	Obtain an answer using algebraic and/or numerical methods.
Suggest	Propose a hypothesis or other possible answer.

Appendix 5

Extended Response – Maximising Your Marks

Here are eight extended response titles typical of those in Paper 2. I have picked four of the Command Terms – Outline, Describe, Discuss and Explain.

Notice how in some of them I have broken each answer up into paragraphs, each paragraph dealing with a different component of the question. This helps to produce a clear and well-structured answer, and also, which is VERY important, helps the examiner to mark it.

Outline the use of restriction enzymes (endonucleases) and DNA ligase in gene technology. [6]

Endonucleases are a particular group of enzymes that cut DNA at specific places. These cuts are asymmetric and result in sticky ends.

sticky end of unpaired bases

DNA ligase is an enzyme that can join pieces of DNA that have corresponding sticky ends.
An example of gene technology is the production of human insulin by modified *E. coli* bacteria. These bacteria contain small circular pieces of DNA called plasmids. Plasmids are removed and cut with a specific endonuclease. The insulin gene is obtained and corresponding sticky ends added. DNA ligase is then used to add the insulin gene to the cut plasmid before the recombinant plasmid is inserted into *E. coli* bacteria. These bacteria are cloned in a suitable medium in order to produce insulin.

Describe the features of alveoli that make them well adapted for gas exchange. [5]

Remember that you can use both blue and black, and using both colours in diagrams and graphs can be helpful.

For the black part of diagrams ALWAYS use an HB pencil.

It is better to label in pencil as well, and use a ruler for the label lines.

Drawings and diagrams should always be large and clear.

Alveoli are the air sacs where gas exchange takes place. Their tiny size gives them a very large surface area to volume ratio and they are covered in a dense network of capillaries. The wall is only one cell thick and the cells are called pneumocytes. There are two types. Type I is the most common and they are especially thin which makes it much more efficient for gas exchange between the blood and alveolar air. Type II secretes a watery solution. This provides a moist surface lining the alveoli which helps gas exchange, and it also contains a surfactant which prevents the walls of the alveoli from sticking together which would reduce the surface area.

Discuss the role played by phagocytic leucocytes (phagocytes) in protecting the body from pathogens. [5]

Phagocytes are a type of white blood cell forming a non-specific defence mechanism in the blood. They attack pathogens in the blood stream but they are also able to leave capillaries and attack pathogens in tissues where they concentrate at sites of infection. They recognize pathogens by detecting foreign protein molecules on the pathogen surface and this is made easier if antibodies have become attached to the pathogen. The phagocyte engulfs the pathogen by phagocytosis to form a vesicle in the cytoplasm. Lysosomes release digestive enzymes into the vesicle to destroy the pathogen.

Explain the processes of active and passive transport that move materials across a membrane. [8]

Active transport is a process which moves substances across a membrane against a concentration gradient and consequently this requires energy from ATP. In addition an integral membrane protein is required which has a specific binding site for the substance to be transported. Some transport proteins transfer more than one specific substance. These substances may be transported in the same direction or, as with the Na^+/K^+ pump in neurons, in opposite directions.

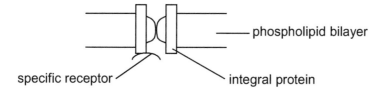

Phagocytosis (transporting particles) and pinocytosis (transporting solution) are ways in which substances can be brought into a cell - endocytosis. Both require energy.

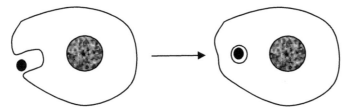

On the other hand passive transport only moves substances across a membrane down the concentration gradient and does not use energy. This is because particles move in a random way and will spread from a region where there is a high concentration to a region where the concentration is lower due to their molecular kinetic energy. Simple diffusion is when substances such as oxygen pass through the phospholipid bilayer. Facilitated diffusion is when an integral protein channel allows a substance to pass across the membrane easily. These channels are specific such as the sodium and potassium ion channels in neurons. Flow through these channels can be controlled if the channel is gated.

Osmosis is the passive movement of water across a membrane. Most water crosses a membrane through specific integral protein channels but some can move by simple diffusion even though the core of membranes is hydrophobic. This is possible because water is sufficiently small.

Explain why enzymes are substrate specific and why their activity is affected by substrate concentration. [8]

Enzymes are large proteins folded into a 3D shape which allows for the formation of an active site where the substrate binds. This active site has a specific shape which corresponds to the shape of the substrate in the same way that a key fits a lock. Furthermore the chemical properties of the active site correspond to the chemical properties of the substrate allowing the two to lock together. The combination of these two points means that an enzyme can only react with a specific substrate.

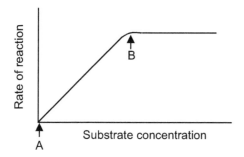

The graph assumes the concentration of the enzyme is fixed. The substrate and enzyme molecules move around randomly and at some point will collide in such a way that the substrate binds to the active site. Between A and B as more substrate is added there is a proportional increase in reaction rate because more collisions are taking place. At point B at any moment in time all the active sites are occupied and so further addition of substrate will have no effect and there can be no further increase in reaction rate.

Explain the control of blood glucose levels in humans. [9]

Blood glucose needs to be kept at a near constant level called the norm. Deviations from this norm are corrected using a negative feedback control mechanism. Blood glucose is monitored by cells in the islets of Langerhans in the pancreas.

If the level of blood glucose rises above the norm as a result of eating sugary or starch foods then beta cells in the islets release the hormone insulin. This circulates in the blood and causes a number of tissues to respond to reduce the blood glucose level. Liver and muscle cells increase their uptake of glucose and convert it into glycogen which can be stored. Adipose tissue cells absorb glucose and convert it into fat. Liver cells can also increase their rate of respiration simply to burn up the excess glucose.

If the level of blood glucose falls then alpha cells in the islets release the hormone glucagon. This stimulates liver cells to break down stored glycogen to release glucose into the blood. Muscle tissue cannot do this. If necessary the adipose tissue can break down fat which can be converted to glucose, and in extreme situations amino acids from the breakdown of protein can be used to make glucose. This is called gluconeogenesis.

Explain the principles of synaptic transmission. [8]

When an impulse arrives at the synaptic terminal it causes depolarisation of the presynaptic membrane. This allows calcium ions to diffuse from the synaptic gap into the presynaptic terminal. This influx of calcium ions causes vesicles of neurotransmitter to move towards and fuse with the presynaptic membrane. Neurotransmitter is released by exocytosis and diffuses across the synaptic gap where it binds to specific receptors on the postsynaptic membrane. This causes channels to open allowing sodium ions to diffuse from the synaptic gap into the postsynaptic terminal depolarising the neuron membrane. This stimulates a postsynaptic action potential.

The neurotransmitter now has to be removed from the synaptic gap. In the case of the neurotransmitter acetyl choline it is broken down by the enzyme acetyl cholinesterase and the end products, acetate and choline, are taken back into the presynaptic terminal to be recycled into new vesicles.
The calcium ions are pumped back into the synaptic gap by active transport.

Explain how the nerve impulse passes along a neuron. [9]

The neuron contains a number of components for transmission of an impulse. These are voltage gated sodium and potassium ion channels (VGNa and VGK channels), open potassium channels, and linked sodium/potassium active pumps.

During the resting potential the pump transports sodium ions out of the axoplasm and potassium ions in. Potassium ions diffuse out of the axoplasm through the open channels. Along with negative ions retained in the axoplasm this produces a resting potential of -70mV across the neuron membrane. When the neuron is stimulated VGNa channels open allowing sodium ions to diffuse in making the axoplasm less negative. If the threshold potential is reached depolarisation continues and the axoplasm reaches a potential of +30mV. This is the first phase of the action potential.

The second phase of the action potential, repolarisation, then occurs. Potassium ions continue to diffuse out of the open channels but the flow is increased due to VGK channels opening. This makes the axoplasm less positive. Finally the active pump removes the sodium ions that diffused in.
In order to propagate a nerve impulse the action potential must occur in the adjacent region of the neuron. Local currents set up in the axoplasm during depolarisation stimulate adjacent VGNa channels to open and this is repeated along the length of the neuron. In a myelinated neuron the action potential only occurs at nodes of Ranvier and so the action potential jumps from node to node. This is called saltatory conduction and transmission is faster than in a non-myelinated neuron.

Appendix 6

Exam Equipment and Mobile Phones

Having invigilated many exams it never ceases to surprise me what vital items students forget to bring in. If you never use an item then fine, but if you need it and haven't got it then it creates stress. If English is not your first language then for some exams you are allowed to take in a basic language dictionary. Check with your IB co-ordinator first though.

I would suggest taking the following into EVERY exam, ie ALL subjects, in a large <u>transparent</u> pencil case –

- ❑ 2 or 3 black pens and blue pens – you can use both in your answers,
- ❑ several spare cartridges if you use liquid ink,
- ❑ highlighters for highlighting key words and points in questions,
- ❑ 15cm transparent ruler with a good clean edge – for labelling drawings,
- ❑ 30cm transparent ruler with a good clean edge – for graphs,
- ❑ 2 HB propelling pencils,
- ❑ clean pencil eraser,
- ❑ compass with a sharp pencil ready fitted,
- ❑ pencil sharpener,
- ❑ set square and protractor,
- ❑ calculator - put new batteries in.

Further calculator points

Check with your Maths teacher that you have a permitted calculator. Certain models are not permitted and could be confiscated. Other models are permitted but have to be set up in a specific exam mode, for example the TI Nspire. Certain programmes and applications are permitted and others are not. If you are found to have an illegal programme / application on your calculator in an exam you may be reported to the Exam Board.

For Paper 1 Multiple Choice papers you are not allowed a calculator but for Paper 2 you are. These papers run consecutively so your exam supervisor will make the arrangements for you to have your calculator for Paper 2.

Mobile phones, iPods and other electronic communication devices

NEVER TAKE THESE INTO THE EXAM ROOM

This is a serious breach of exam regulations and you may have that exam paper removed from your record.

This could mean <u>failing your Diploma</u>.

Good luck!

Acknowledgements

Links to third party websites are provided by OSC in good faith and for information only. OSC disclaims any responsibility for the materials contained in any third party website referenced in this work.

Chapter 2

© Shutterstock, chapter image, 2.1; 2.2; 2.3; 2.4; Image courtesy of André Brown and John Weisel, MRC Laboratory of Molecular Biology, 2.5; © Ashby Merson-Davies, 2.6; 2.7.

Chapter 3

© Ashby Merson-Davies, 3.1; 3.25a & b; With kind permission of Larry Phelps, University of Wisconsin, 3.35; © Shutterstock, chapter image, 3.2; 3.4; 3.5; 3.6; 3.7; 3.8a & b; 3.9; 3.10; 3.11; 3.12; 3.15b; 3.23; 3.32; 3.34; Flyingdream at en.wikipedia [Public domain or Public domain], from Wikimedia Commons, 3.3; Images courtesy of Dr Paul Verkade in the Bristol Bio Imaging Centre of Bristol University, 3.13; 3.16; 3.21; Images courtesy of John Pacy, King's College Electron Microscopy Unit, 3.14; 3.15a; 3.18; 3.19a & b; 3.27; © Don W. Fawcett/SCIENCE PHOTO LIBRARY, 3.17, 3.20; Image courtesy of Professor Anton Page, Biomedical Imaging Unit, University of Southampton, 3.22; Boghog2 (Boghog2 work) [Public domain], via Wikimedia Commons, 3.24; © Rob Cowie / Wikimedia Commons / CC-BY-SA-3.0 / GFDL, 3.26; © American Society of Plant Biologists. Reprinted with permission, 3.28; and3k and caper437 (Own work by uploaders) [CC-BY-SA-3.0 (http://creativecommons.org/licenses/by-sa/3.0) or GFDL (http://www.gnu.org/copyleft/fdl.html)], via Wikimedia Commons, 3.29a; © Don W. Fawcett/SCIENCE PHOTO LIBRARY, 3.29b; By Afunguy at en.wikipedia [Public domain], via Wikimedia Commons, 3.30; staticd (Own work) [CC-BY-SA-3.0 (http://creativecommons.org/licenses/by-sa/3.0)], via Wikimedia Commons, 3.31; Image courtesy of Brian Leatherbarrow *FRCS FRCOphth*, 3.33.

Chapter 4

Donald Nicholson ©2002 International Union of Biochemistry and Molecular Biology, chapter image. © Shutterstock, 4.1; Calvin, M. (1948). *The path of carbon in photosynthesis*. Berkeley, Ca.: [Lawrence] Radiation Laboratory, Hathi Digital Library. http://babel.hathitrust.org/cgi/pt?id=mdp.39015086549345;view=1up;seq=1, 4.2; http://www.flickr.com/people/fanny/ (http://www.flickr.com/photos/fanny/555925/) [CC-BY-SA-2.0 (http://creativecommons.org/licenses/by-sa/2.0)], via Wikimedia Commons, 4.3; © BIOPHOTO ASSOCIATES/SCIENCE PHOTO LIBRARY, 4.4.

Chapter 5

© Ashby Merson-Davies, 5.1; 5.2a; 5.3a & b; 5.8; 5.10a & b; 5.11a & b; 5.13; 5.16a & b; 5.18; © Shutterstock, chapter image, 5.2b; 5.4a & b; 5.5; 5.6; 5.9a & b; 5.12; 5.15; 5.17; 5.19 a & b; Ed Uthman [CC BY 2.0 (http://creativecommons.org/licenses/by/2.0)], via Wikimedia Commons, 5.7; Image courtesy of André Brown and John Weisel, MRC Laboratory of Molecular Biology, 5.14; Pixabay, 5.20.

Chapter 6

© Shutterstock, chapter image; © JUANCITO (Remonta Inesperado), el mejor mulo de la Argentina, de expedición en Península Mitre, Tierra del Fuego, 6.1; © Ashby Merson-Davies, 6.2; 6.5; 6.6; 6.8; 6.10; 6.13. Pixabay, 6.3; Photo courtesy of Dr Pavel Kratina, Queen Mary University of London, School of Biological and Chemical Sciences, 6.7a; Photo courtesy of Dr Philip Fay, Environmental Science Institute, University of Texas, 6.7b; By NASA [Public domain], via Wikimedia Commons, 6.9; Dr Pieter Tans, NOAA/ESRL (www.esrl.noaa.gov/gmd/ccgg/trends/) and Dr Ralph Keeling, Scripps Institution of Oceanography (scrippsco2.ucsd.edu/), 6.11; Temperature:ftp://ftp.ncdc.noaa.gov/pub/data/anomoalies/annual_land.and.ocean.ts Data source CO_2 (Siple Ice Cores):http://cdiac.esd.ornl.gov/ftp/trends/co2/siple2.013 Data source CO_2(Mauna Loa):http://cdiac.esd.ornl.gov/ftp/trends.co2/maunaloa.co2, 6.12; Photo by Nancy Daschbach, NOAA, 6.14.

Chapter 7

© Shutterstock, chapter image, 7.1; 7.4; 7.11; alpsdake (Own work) [Public domain], via Wikimedia Commons, 7.2; From Proc. N.A.S Vol.55 1966, Autoradiography of chromosomal DNA fibres from Chinese hamster cells. Joel A. Huberman and Arthur D. Riggs, Reprinted with the kind permission of Dr Riggs and Professor Huberman, 7.3; Reproduced with the kind permission of Alec Jeffreys, Wellcome Images, 7.5; © 2012 Edvotek Inc. All rights reserved. www.edvotek.com, 7.7; © Ashby Merson-Davies, 7.8, 7.9; Pixabay, 7.10.

Chapter 8

© Pixabay, 8.1b; 8.13a; 8.13b; 8.13d; 8.14a; 8.14b; Conrad Martens (1801-21 August 1878) [Public domain], via Wikimedia Commons, 8.1c; See page for author [Public domain or Public domain], via Wikimedia Commons, 8.2; Brian Gratwicke Flickr Creative Commons; 8.3a & b; © Ashby Merson-Davies, 8.4; 8.5; 8.6; 8.9; 8.11; 8.12a - f; 8.13e; 9.13f; 8.13g; 8.13h; 8.14c; 8.14d; 8.14e; Reprinted from Kettlewell, H. B. D. Thanks to Professor Peter Holland, Department of Zoology, South Parks Road, Oxford, OX1 3PS, 8.7a; 8.7b 4652 Paces Flickr Creative Commons, 8.8; © Corrian Homan Design Studio, 8.10; © Shutterstock, chapter image 8.14.

MID IBDP SUMMER PROGRAMMES

OSC

Summary

Who is it for?
For students entering their final year of the IB Diploma Programme

Locations include:
Harvard and MIT, USA
Cambridge, UK

Duration
Min. 1 week, max. 6 weeks
1 or 2 IB subjects per week

Improve confidence and grades

Highly-experienced IB teachers and examiners

Tailored classes to meet students' needs

Wide range of available subjects

Safe accommodation and 24-hour pastoral care

Features

- Morning teaching in chosen IB subject
- 2nd IB subject afternoon classes
- IB Skills afternoon classes
- One-to-one Extended Essay Advice, Private Tuition and University Guidance options
- Small classes
- Daily homework
- Unique IB university fair
- Class reports for parents
- Full social programme.

By the end of their first year, students understand the stimulating and challenging nature of the IB Diploma.

They also know that the second year is crucial in securing the required grades to get into their dream college or university.

This course helps students to avoid a 'summer dip' by using their time effectively. With highly-experienced IB teachers, we consolidate a student's year one

learning, close knowledge gaps, and introduce some year two material.

In a relaxed environment, students develop academically through practice revision and review. They are taught new skills, techniques, and perspectives – giving a real boost to their grades. This gives students an enormous amount of confidence and drive for their second year.

The whole experience was incredible. The university setting was inspiring, the friends I made, and the teaching was first-class. I feel so much more confident in myself and in my subject.

OSC Student

Please note that locations and course features are subject to change - please check our website for up-to-date details.

Find out more: osc-ib.com/mid +44 (0)1865 512802